Spotlight SCIENCE

FOR SCOTLAND

S1

★ **Keith JOHNSON** ★ **Gareth WILLIAMS**
★ **Sue ADAMSON** ★ **Derek McMONAGLE**

With the active support of: Lawrie Ryan, Bob Wakefield, Anne Goldsworthy, Roger Frost, Helen Davis, Valerie Wood-Robinson, Phil Bunyan, John Bailey, Adrian Wheaton, Janet Hawkins, Ann Johnson, Graham Adamson, Diana Williams, Shenaz Ahktar, Hilda Dalziel, Roseleen Kennedy, Karen Miller, Moira Russell, David Lawson, Paul McGorry.

5-14 EDITION

First published in 2002 by:
Nelson Thornes Ltd
Delta Place
27 Bath Road
CHELTENHAM
GL53 7TH
United Kingdom

02 03 04 05 06 / 10 9 8 7 6 5 4 3 2 1

A catalogue record for this book is available from the British Library

ISBN 0 7487 7047 X

Illustrations by Jane Cope and Peters & Zabransky
Page make-up by Tech-set

Printed and bound in Italy by Canale

Acknowledgements

The authors and publishers are grateful to the following for permission to reproduce photographs:

Action Plus: Glynn Kirk 149; A&R Scott: 18R; Ace Photolibrary International: 157M; AEA Technology: 104L; Ann Ronan Picture Library: 37, 199B; Aquarius Pictures: 144; Associated Press: Becker & Bredel 187T; Axon Images: 4BR, 7, 8BR, 82ML, 82MR, 168T; Bart's Medical Picture Library: 145R; Biophoto Associates: 31ML, 35, 36MR, 148B; BP AMOCO: 212M; Bridgeman Art Library: Musée d'Orsay, Paris, France / Bulloz 45, Edelfelt, AGA 179; British Airways: 207L; British Caledonian: 4BCT; Bruce Coleman: Jules Cowan 32ML, Dr Eckart Pott 32B, Frank Greenaway 109R, Rod Williams 111, Eric Crichton 127, Jane Burton 155TL, Neil McAllister 155B, John Cancalosi 159MB, John R Anthony 172ML, John Markham 172MC, Jane Burton 181BL, 186B, Jane Burton 181BL; Bruno Gardent: 137; Bubbles Photolibrary: 201(4), 143; CEFIC: 129; Chris Fairclough Colour Library: 182; Chubb: 153B; Collections: Anthea Sieveking 165TR, MR, B, 68, 107; Colorsport: Stewart Fraser 169B; Corbis: 169T, BR, ML; Corel (NT): 4BCL, 4BCR, 6T, 8TR, 24T, 31MR, 31BL, 48TL, 48TR, 82BR, BL, 88TR, 105TL,131L, R, 161B 162TR, BR, 164BL, 165TL, B, 166L, 172T, 185ML, MR, R, 200; Cotswold Wildlife Park: 30TL, ML, MR; Diamar (NT): 81; Digital Stock (NT): 58BR, 152; Digital Vision (NT): 28MC, 30BL, 31TL, 33B, 48BL, 58BC, 118B, 156, 157B, 192, 205, 214; DUPONT: 4T; Ecoscene: Anthony Cooper 168BL; Empics: Tony Marshall 13L; Eye Ubiquitous: James Davis Worldwide 151, 189; Fisons: 114BL; Ford: 48BR; Frank Lane Picture Agency: W Howes 33T, 36TR, W Wisniewski 42T, Tom & Pam; Gardener 97, Celtic Picture Agency 159B, M Walker: 166BR; Gary M Prior: 138T, 141; Geophotos: 160T, M, 161T, 170MR; Geoscience Features Picture Library: 155TR, MR, ML, 157TL, TC, TR, 158M, L, TR, BR, 159TL, TR, 160BL, BR, 170ML, MC, 219; Getty Images: Chad Slattery, Stone 24B, Jamie McDonald 49L, David Norton, Telegraph Colour Library 69; Glaxosmithklinebeecham: 133; Heinz: 82BCR; Historic Scotland: 162L; Holt Studios International: 114BR; ICI: 11B, 87, 201B, Chemicals & Polymers 212T; J W Branagan: 76; James Longley: 168BR; Jane Burton: 175T; Jean Francois Causse: 16; John P A Carter: 43; John Walmsley: 20, 58TR, 65TL; London Fire Brigade: 79; London Illustrated News: 139, 198TR; Martyn Chillmaid: 5T, 6M, 22L, 22R, 41, 67, 72TL, BL, 82TL, TR, MC, 84, 86, 93, 90, 118TL, TR, 128L, R, 130, 134T, B, 136, 153T, 178B, 180B, 181T, 198TL, 198B, 199TL, TCL, TCR, TR, M, 201TL, TR, 1,2,3,5,6, 206, 207C, 208TL, TR, B, 209L, R, 210, 211L, R; Michael Scott: 119; Moorfields Eye Hospital: 72TR; NASA: 13R, TR, 187B, 190TR, BL, 191TR, 194BR, BL, 195MR, ML, 196; National Motor Museum: 48TC; Natural History Photographic Agency: Agence Nature 172MR, Stephen Dalton 180T; Natural Visions: 28TC, TR, 32MR, 95, 185L; Oxford Scientific Films: G I Bernard 28BL, 28BR, Alistair Shay 28BCL, Tim Sheppard 32T, 36TL, ML, 145L, Mark Ulrich 175B; Photodisc (NT): 8L, 28TL, 28MR, BCR, 30TR, 31MC, BR, 46B, 58BL, 62T, 82MC, BCL, 106TL, TR, 108, 109L, 166M, 217; Photographers Library: 117; Pilot Publishers Services Ltd.: 212B; Planet Earth Pictures: 176; Procter & Gamble: 82TC; Quadrant: 114T; Rex Features: Today 14; Roger Labrosse: 150T; Ron Sutherland: 57; Ronald Grant Archive: 195B; Royal Mint: 4BL; Science Photolibrary: 6B, 147, 148T, 183, 191TL, Bruce Iverson 34T, Andrew Syred 34B, Chuck Brown 42, David Scharf 46T, 54TL, John Samford 184, Nestle, Petit Fomat 60L, 62ML, MR, B, Don Fawcett 61, Katrina Thomas 64, Alex Bartel 72BR, 142, Oscar Burriel, Latin Stock 96, Dr K F R Schiller 101, Gordon Garradd 102, Hattie Young 110T, Shiela Terry 118TC, Larry Mulverhill 137B, John Radcliffe Hospital 146, Sinclair Stammers 159MT, Michael Marten 164T, Sidney Moulds 178T, Claude Nuridsany & Marie Perennou 178M Alfred Pasieka 181BR, 216, NASA 190TL, 191ML, USGS, 190BR, John Chumack 194TL, Royal Observatory, Edinburgh 194TR, Novosti 195T; Scottish Hydroelectric: 23; Scottish National Blood Transfusion Service: 150B; Sea Life Centre: 30BR; Silvercross Ltd.: 56B; Stephen Munday: 138B; Stockmarket: 56T, ZEFA 88BR; ZEFA: Kalt 174a, b, c, d.
Picture research by johnbailey@axonimages.com and Stuart Sweatmore. Every effort has been made to trace all copyright holders but if any have been overlooked the publisher will be pleased to make the necessary arrangements at the first opportunity.

Contents

▶ Look at some of the words we use to describe materials.

- In your group, choose one of the words. You need to explain to other groups what the word means.
  BUT … You cannot use the word itself!
  You cannot use the opposite of the word!

- Write down an explanation of your chosen word on a piece of paper. You can also draw pictures to give clues.

  If there is time you can do this with other words from the list.

- Now swap pieces of paper with other groups.
  Look at the explanations and pictures.
  Try to guess what the words are.

  If you think that other groups have good explanations, make a note of them. This may be useful for **Things to do** question 2.

Soft Weak **HARD** smooth soluble Rough flexible Stretchy shiny STRONG DULL

Properties of materials

As you have already discovered, each material has its own set of **properties**. You have been using words which describe properties. For example, the properties of rubber could be:

it is smooth, it is dull, it is flexible and it is stretchy.

Remember that a **property** must describe *any* piece of the material.

▶ Think about the materials chosen for the items in these photographs.

For each one, write down at least 2 properties which make it a suitable material.

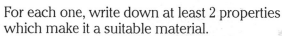

What a disaster!

There will be some disasters here!

▶ Look at these pictures of materials in use in 4 different situations.

In each case say why the material shown is not suitable.

Suggest a better material for use in each case.

A What do you think about concrete shoes?

B Have you ever driven across a rubber bridge?

C Do you have wooden pans at home?

D Would you like a steel pillow?

How strong?

Plywood is made of a few thin sheets of wood glued together.
Ann says "Plywood can't be as strong as one solid piece of wood."
How could you test Ann's idea?
Write a plan for your test.
How could you make your results reliable?

1 Give 2 examples in each case of materials which are:
a) strong   b) flexible   c) soft.

2 You can make your own properties dictionary.
Write a list of 10 words used to describe materials.
Put the words in alphabetical order.
Write a sentence to explain the meaning of each word.
Draw pictures if this helps you to explain.

3 Make a simple drawing of a bicycle. Add labels to show the materials used to make the various parts.

4 Write down 3 uses of each of these materials:
a) wood
b) plastic
c) metal
d) glass
e) concrete.

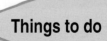

5 Do a survey of the ways in which food is packaged. Look at home or in a shop to see what types of containers are used.
a) What materials are used for the packaging?
b) Why are these materials suitable?
c) Do you think all the packaging is always needed?

Things to do

What's in a material?

The ancient Greeks thought that all substances were made up of 4 things:
- earth
- air
- fire
- water.

They thought that these things were joined together in different amounts to make different materials.

▶ Do you agree with this idea?

   Discuss it in your group.

Look at the photographs of structures from Lego.
Lego pieces are simple blocks which can be combined in different ways.
The same blocks can be made into many different objects.

In the same way all the materials used in the world are made from simple substances.
These simple substances can be combined in different ways to make different materials.

In 1661 Robert Boyle gave a name to the simplest substances.
He called them **elements**.
Scientists still use this description.

An element is a substance which cannot be broken down into anything simpler.

You will find out more about elements later in the course.

There are over 100 elements.
92 of these are found naturally on Earth.
The same elements can combine in different ways.
Many different materials can be made.
The elements carbon, hydrogen and oxygen can combine to make sugar or to make the acid in vinegar.

Naming materials

Look at the objects on display. They are made from different materials.
How many of these materials do you know?
List the names of as many as possible.

Most of the materials are made from elements combined together.
Some are made from *only one* element.

Can you guess which objects on display are made from *only one element*?
Can you name the element in each case?
Write down your ideas.

Combining elements

You are going to combine two elements – magnesium and oxygen (from the air).

a What does the magnesium look like?

b What does the oxygen look like?

Stand a Bunsen burner on a heat-resistant mat.
Light the burner. Then make the air-hole half open.
Get a short piece of magnesium ribbon from your teacher.
Hold it at arm's length in some tongs.
Move the magnesium ribbon into the flame (do not look directly at it).

Observe what happens.

Magnesium has now combined with the oxygen.

c What does the new material look like?

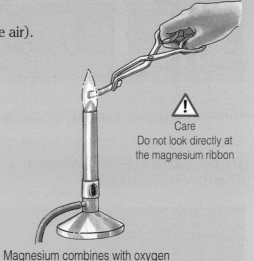

⚠️ Care
Do not look directly at
the magnesium ribbon

Magnesium combines with oxygen
in the air. It makes a new material.

Removing elements

Copper carbonate is made from the elements copper, carbon and oxygen.
Put 4 spatula measures of copper carbonate in a test-tube.
Heat it with a normal Bunsen burner flame.

Observe what happens.

d What did the copper carbonate look like at the start?
e What does the substance look like at the end?

The copper carbonate **loses** something during the heating.
It loses some carbon and some oxygen.

f Where do you think these elements have gone? Try to explain.

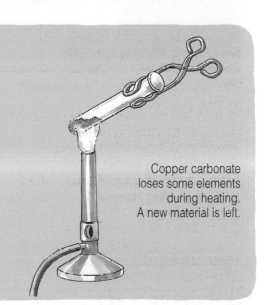

Copper carbonate
loses some elements
during heating.
A new material is left.

Things to do

1 Copy and complete using the words in the box.

| element | combined | carbon |
| oxygen | copper | 100 |

a) A substance which cannot be broken down into anything simpler is an . . . .
b) All substances are made from elements . . . . in different ways.
c) There are more than . . . . elements.
d) Copper carbonate is made of 3 elements:
. . . ., ... and . . . .

2 Which of these substances are elements?
copper, carbon dioxide, oxygen, iron, sodium chloride, tin, magnesium, magnesium oxide, copper carbonate

3 Sometimes when elements combine, it's bad news.
What happens to iron when it combines with oxygen in damp weather?
Write about the problems caused by this.

Making new materials

Some materials are **natural**. Others are **made**.

All these materials are made from **elements**.

Sometimes the elements are already combined in nature to give us a useful material.

The wool from a sheep is a **natural** material. Why is it useful**?**

The wood from a tree is a **natural** material. Why is it useful**?**

Sometimes scientists combine the elements in new ways. This is to make a useful material. The material is **synthetic**.

Glass is a **synthetic** material. It can be made from sand and sodium carbonate.

Just the job!

Some of the clothes you wear are made from natural materials. Examples are cotton, wool and silk.
Other clothes are made from **synthetic** (made) materials. Examples are polyester and acrylic.
You may have some clothes made of a mixture of materials. An example is polyester and cotton.

Different materials have different properties. Look at the pictures here. For each one, say which properties the material used for the clothing should have.

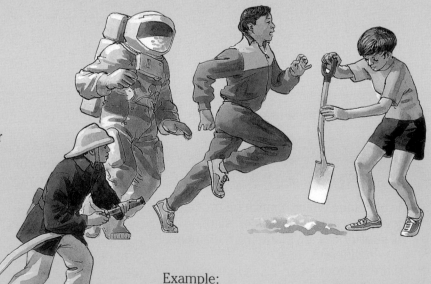

Example:
Ideally T-shirts should be made of material which is light and lets body heat out.

When you buy a piece of clothing you need to think about how you will use it. The type of material may be important.

Maybe you want to be ... just fashionable,
  ... warm,
  ... dry?

In the next investigation you can compare 2 different materials used to make clothes.

Comparing a natural and a synthetic material

Your teacher will give you a sample of 2 materials.
One of these is natural. The other is synthetic.

In your group plan an investigation to compare the materials.
You could design tests to see which material will ...

or (a) keep you drier
    (b) keep you warmer.

Choose one of the ideas.

flammable

Write down your plan.

You need to include details of:
- the apparatus you will need
- what you will do (include safety points)
- what measurements or observations you will make
- how you will make your results reliable
- how you will present your results.

Your plan should be shown to your teacher before you start practical work.

If there is time, your teacher may let you plan and do another test.

You might need

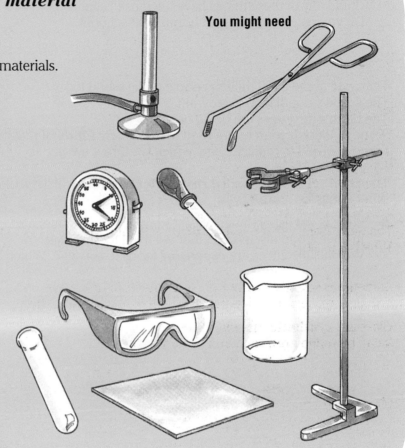

---

1 Copy the table into your book. Write down 3 materials in each column.

Natural	Synthetic (made)

2 Find out about the story of **either** cotton **or** silk.
Where is the material found?
Where is it made?
How is it changed for us to use?

3 Do a survey of your clothes at home.
- Look at the label to see what your clothes are made of.
- What does the material feel like? (soft, rough, smooth, etc.)
- Are there any special care instructions, e.g. for washing or drying?
Record your findings in a table.
From your list say:
a) which material can be washed at the highest temperature.
b) which material feels the roughest.

Things to do

Using materials

We use up lots of material every day.

▶ Think about what you have done since you got up this morning.
  Make a list of all the things you've thrown away.
  Could any of these things have been used again?
  Do you recycle anything at home or at school?

There are about 7000 million people in the world today.
The world's population is growing.
The Earth's resources are being used up.
Some of these resources are used to make new **kinds** of materials.
Some are used to replace items which we throw away.

The Earth's resources are the **raw materials** from which we make other things.

▶ Look at the list of things we get from some raw materials.
  In your group discuss whether we need these things.
  Which substances are **essential** for us to survive? Which are not?

Substance from raw material	Raw material
salt	sea
oxygen	air
plastics	coal, crude oil, natural gas
copper	rocks
vegetable oil	living things (plants)

A scientific enquiry

Look at the Task Questions on the opposite page.
Choose 1 of these questions to investigate.
Carry out a scientific enquiry.

Think about:
- where you will get the information from
  (try to use more than one source)

- how you will present your findings
  (diagrams, tables, charts or graphs?).

Make sure that you:
- look at all the evidence and information
- make a conclusion (answer the question)
- consider whether your evidence is reliable
  (are you sure this is the right conclusion?).

Task Question *Artificial fertiliser – friend or enemy?*

Carry out an enquiry to answer this question.

These are some of the questions you could answer to help your enquiry:

- What is a fertiliser?
- What are the raw materials used to make fertiliser?
- How are artificial fertilisers made?
- Why do we need artificial fertilisers?
- How much artificial fertiliser is used each year in the UK?
- How much does artificial fertiliser cost?
- What are the disadvantages of using artificial fertiliser?

Task Question *Recycling – is it worth it?*

Carry out an enquiry to answer this question.

These are some of the questions you could answer to help your enquiry:

- What is recycling?
- Which materials are recycled in the UK?
- Why do people choose to recycle?
- What does the recycling process involve?
- How much does it cost to recycle materials?
- In the UK, what percentage of waste is recycled?
- Why isn't more waste recycled?

1 Some of the Earth's resources have many uses.
Crude oil is an important resource.
It is a mixture of many substances.
The percentage of each substance is shown in this table:

Name of substance in crude oil	% of substance in crude oil
fuel gas	2
petrol	6
naphtha	10
kerosine	13
diesel oil	19
fuel and bitumen	50

a) Draw a bar-chart to show this information.
b) Choose 4 of the substances found in crude oil. Draw pictures to show a use for each of them.

2 Look at the table of raw materials on the opposite page. Which of the 5 could be used to get:
a) sugar?   c) nitrogen?
b) iron?   d) pure water?

3 Some synthetic materials can be helpful or harmful.
Write about the helpful and harmful uses of:
a) detergents
b) medicines
c) explosives.

Things to do

11

Questions

1 Choose one of the following materials:

      gold   paper   glass
         wood   plastic

Collect pictures from newspapers and
magazines to show your material in use in
different objects.

2 Look at the picture of a playground and choose 6 objects which
could be made from different materials.
Copy out this table and complete it for each of your objects.

Object	Material used to make it	Raw materials from which the material is made

3 Crude oil is an important raw material.
What do you know about crude oil?
Write down as many things as you can.

4 Mrs Walker is planning to decorate Neil's bedroom.
Neil is two years old and messy!
Mrs Walker has 3 samples of wallpaper which the
adverts say are 'easy to clean'.
a) Plan an investigation to find out which wallpaper
is the easiest to clean.
b) What other factors might Mrs Walker consider
before buying the paper?

5 The contents of your school wastebins have been surveyed.
The results are shown in the table. A group of pupils wants to find
out if the waste can be recycled.
a) Draw a bar-chart of these results.
b) What percentage of the waste is plastic?
c) Where do you think most of the waste aluminium came from?
d) Do you think it's worth recycling materials?
Why? Why not?
e) How would you encourage pupils in school to recycle waste?

Type of waste	Number of items
paper	85
glass	45
aluminium	30
other metals	5
plastic	30
other	5

6 Think about the type of material used to make the drainpipes on
a new house.
Make a list of the properties this material should have.

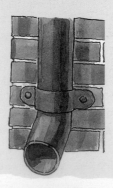

Energy

Without energy nothing can ever happen!

All living things need energy to stay alive and to move. You get your energy from your food.

Machines cannot work without energy.

Electricity is a very convenient form of energy.

In this topic:

What is energy?

We often use the word '**energy**'.
Tina says, "I've got lots of energy today."
John says, "I haven't got enough energy to climb the hill."
A car driver says, "I need some more petrol – my car has almost run out of energy."

▶ Write down three sentences of your own, using the word 'energy'.

▶ What do you think the word 'energy' means?
Where do you get your energy from?

▶ Look at the photograph. How many examples of energy can you find? Make a list.

Energy diagrams

Energy is needed to get jobs done, or make things work.
To get a job done, energy must be moved or **transferred** from one place to another?

Example 1
Suppose you wind up a clockwork toy, and then let it run across the table.
Where are the energy transfers?

start
energy stored in your body → energy stored in the wound-up spring → movement energy of the toy

This is an **Energy Transfer Diagram**.

Example 2
Sometimes an Energy Transfer Diagram splits into two or more parts.
Suppose you switch on a torch:

energy stored in the battery → energy lighting up the room / energy heating up the bulb

The energy heating up the bulb is **wasted** energy. It is not useful.

Example 3
Rub your hands together quickly about 20 times.
What do you notice? Copy and complete this energy diagram:

. . . . stored in my . . . . → movement energy of my hands → energy . . . . up my hands / . . . . of the sound made by my hands

Energy transfers

Try each of these experiments and observe them carefully.
Think about the energy transfers. For each one:
- sketch a diagram of the equipment, and
- draw an Energy Transfer Diagram.

a a clockwork car

b a battery and a lamp bulb

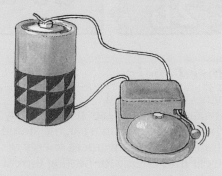

c a battery and a buzzer or door-bell

d a Bunsen burner

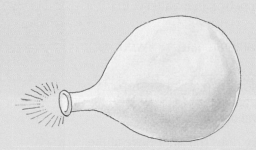

e blow up a balloon and
then release it

f a dynamo and a lamp

Measuring energy

Sometimes we need to measure the amount of energy. The unit we use for measuring energy is the **joule**. This is written as **J** for short.

The joule is named after James Joule (1818–1889) who did many experiments on energy.

A joule is a small unit of energy. To lift an apple from the floor up on to a table needs about 1 joule of energy.

But if you **eat** the apple, it will give you a lot of energy – about 200 000 joules of energy. That's enough energy to walk up 50 flights of stairs!

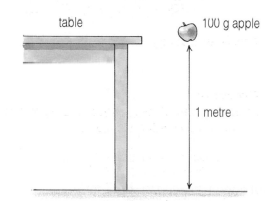

table   100 g apple

1 metre

---

1 Copy and complete:
a) . . . . is needed to get jobs done.
b) Energy is measured in . . . .

2 Draw a diagram to show the energy transfers when you pedal a bicycle.
Label it clearly.
How do you think it will change if you oil your bike?

3 Draw an Energy Transfer Diagram for a battery-powered television set.

4 Draw Energy Transfer Diagrams for:
a) a girl firing an arrow from a bow
b) a boy kicking a football
c) a bonfire burning
d) a firework rocket
e) a petrol-powered car.

Things to do

Go with energy

Stored energy

Energy can be stored.
For example, petrol has stored energy.
When petrol burns in a car, the stored energy
is transferred to movement energy of
the car **and** energy for heating the car:

Stored energy is often called **potential energy**.

Here are some examples of stored energy:

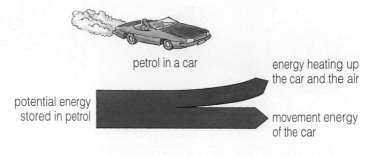

petrol in a car

potential energy stored in petrol

energy heating up the car and the air

movement energy of the car

- **Chemical energy**   For example: in petrol; in a battery; in the food that you eat.

- **Strain energy**   For example: in a catapult; in a clockwork car; in a balloon that has been blown up.

- **Gravitational energy**   For example: if you are at the top of a ladder, you have gravitational potential energy.
  If you fall off the ladder, the energy will damage you!

- Look at the photograph. What energy does the skier have at the top of the hill?

  When she skis down, this potential energy is transferred to her movement energy. (Another name for movement energy is **kinetic energy**.)

▶ Look back at experiments **a–f** on the previous page.
  Where is the stored energy in each one? Make a list.

potential energy ➡ kinetic energy

The energy laws

Here is an energy diagram for a battery connected to an electric motor:

If we measure the amount of energy (in joules) **before** the
transfer and **after** the transfer, we find **it is the same amount**.

In the diagram, 100 joules of energy stored in the battery is
transferred to 70 joules of movement energy and 30 joules
of energy heating up the motor.
So: 100 = 70 + 30, the same amount of energy.

However, only 70 joules of energy are useful to us, as movement
energy. The other 30 J are wasted, because they are no use to us.

This is what happens in energy transfers.
Although there is the same amount of energy afterwards, not all of it is useful.

This is summed up in the 2 laws of energy:

model racing car

100 J
potential energy
stored in the
battery

70 J
movement
energy

30 J
energy heating
up the motor
(wasted energy)

Law 1 The total amount of energy in the universe stays the same. It is 'conserved'. Energy cannot be created or destroyed.	*Law 2* In energy transfers, the energy spreads out, to more and more places. As it spreads, it becomes less useful to us.

A steam engine

Look carefully at a steam engine doing a job of work.

**steam engine
lifting a weight**

steam engine

fuel

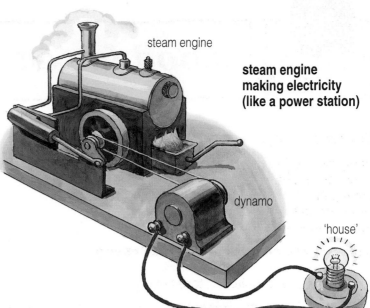

steam engine

**steam engine
making electricity
(like a power station)**

dynamo

'house'

▶ Observe each one carefully and look for energy transfers.
Draw an Energy Transfer Diagram for each one. Try to include
all of the energy changes.

Investigating a clockwork toy

Plan an investigation to see how the **distance travelled** by a
clockwork toy depends on **how much it is wound up**.

- How will you measure the distance accurately?
- Will you wind it up in full-turn steps or half-turn steps?
- How will you ensure it is a **fair test**?
- How can you make your results more reliable?

Ask your teacher to check your plan. How can you improve it?

---

1 Copy and complete:
a) Stored energy is also called . . . . energy.
b) This includes chemical . . . . , ... energy
and . . . . energy.
c) An Energy . . . . Diagram shows us how
the energy is . . . .
d) The amount of . . . . before the transfer is
always . . . . to the amount of energy
. . . . the transfer.

2 A battery is connected to a lamp bulb.
Draw an Energy Transfer Diagram for this.
While it is switched on, the battery gives out
100 joules of energy. If 80 J are heating up
the room, how many joules are lighting the
room?

3 Which of these two words could you
use for each of these examples – **potential**
(stored) energy or **kinetic** (movement)
energy:
a) a can of petrol?
b) a car travelling down a road?
c) water at the very top of a waterfall?
d) water at the bottom of a waterfall?
e) a stretched bow with the arrow about to
be released?
f) the arrow half-way to the target?
g) a rock at the top of a cliff?
h) the rock falling, half-way down?

4 Use the internet, or an encyclopedia, to
find out about the life of James Joule.

Things to do

Food for energy

You need energy for running, sitting, breathing and even for sleeping.
In fact, everything you do needs energy.

You get your energy from your food. The food you eat is your fuel.
Almost everything you eat contains energy.

Energy in food is measured in **kilojoules (kJ)**, where **1 kilojoule = 1000 joules**.

cornflakes with milk
700 kJ

yoghurt
400 kJ

sausage roll
1500 kJ

chips
1000 kJ

tea, milk and sugar
200 kJ

▶ Look at the potential energy in these foods.

a How much energy is there in a breakfast of cornflakes, yoghurt and a cup of tea?

b How much energy is there in a meal of chips and 2 sausage rolls?

How much energy?

The energy stored in foods is often shown on the label.
It is usually shown in kilojoules (**kJ**), and also in kilocalories (kcal).
(kcal is a unit of energy often used in slimming diets.)

▶ Look at these food labels.

c Why is the energy given for 100 grams of each food?

d Which of these foods has the lowest energy per 100 g?

e What happens if the food you eat contains more energy than you need?

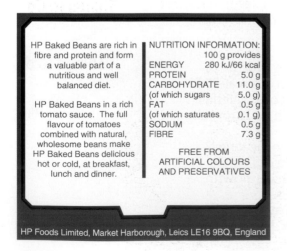

HP Baked Beans are rich in fibre and protein and form a valuable part of a nutritious and well balanced diet.

HP Baked Beans in a rich tomato sauce. The full flavour of tomatoes combined with natural, wholesome beans make HP Baked Beans delicious hot or cold, at breakfast, lunch and dinner.

NUTRITION INFORMATION:

	100 g provides
ENERGY	280 kJ/66 kcal
PROTEIN	5.0 g
CARBOHYDRATE	11.0 g
(of which sugars	5.0 g)
FAT	0.5 g
(of which saturates	0.1 g)
SODIUM	0.5 g
FIBRE	7.3 g

FREE FROM ARTIFICIAL COLOURS AND PRESERVATIVES

HP Foods Limited, Market Harborough, Leics LE16 9BQ, England

NUTRITION
Sainsbury's Sardines in Brine are a good source of Calcium and Vitamin D, both needed for strong bones and teeth; Vitamin B$_{12}$, required for healthy blood and nervous system, Niacin which helps food to give us energy.

	TYPICAL VALUES PER 100 g (3½ oz) OF DRAINED PRODUCT
ENERGY	170 kCALORIES 705 kJOULES
PROTEIN	23.4 g
CARBOHYDRATE	less than 0.1 g
TOTAL FAT	8.3 g
ADDED SALT	0.5 g
VITAMINS/ MINERALS	% OF RECOMMENDED DAILY AMOUNT
NIACIN	45%
VITAMIN B$_{12}$	1400%
VITAMIN D	300%
CALCIUM	110%
IRON	25%

Est.1880

Scott's Porage Oats

THE ORIGINAL SCOTTISH-MILLED OATS

INGREDIENTS

100% **Scott's** Rolled Oats

NUTRITION INFORMATION

Typical values	per 100g	per 30g serving with 210ml skimmed milk
Energy	1540kJ/ 368kcal	760kJ/ 181kcal
Protein	11.0g	10.2g
Carbohydrate	62.0g	28.7g
(of which sugars)	1.1g	10.4g
Fat	8.0g	2.6g
(of which saturates)	1.5g	0.7g
Fibre	7.0g	2.1g
(of which soluble)	3.6g	1.1g
(of which insoluble)	3.4g	1.0g
Sodium	Trace	0.2g

This pack contains 33 servings.

GUARANTEE OF SATISFACTION

Investigating the energy in food

One way of measuring the amount of energy in some food is to burn it.

As the food burns, it gives out energy. We can use this energy to heat up some water.

The more energy stored in the food, the more energy is released and the hotter the water gets.

Plan an investigation to compare the energy content of a peanut with that of a pea.

- What apparatus will you need?
- What measurements will you take?
- How will you record your results?

Remember you must make it a **fair test**, and work safely.

When you have had your plan checked by your teacher, go ahead and do the investigation.

What do you find?

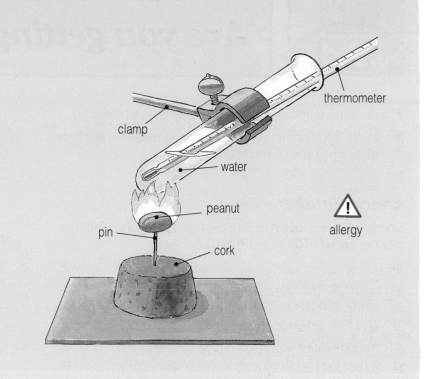

1 For the next 24 hours, keep a record of all the food that you eat.
Next lesson you can use this to work out how much energy you have taken in.

2 Make a survey of how much energy is in different foods. Look at the food labels on packets and cans at home. List them under 'high energy food' or 'low energy food'.

3 Look at the bar-chart.
It shows the energy content in kilojoules for one gram of each food.
a) Which food gives the most energy?
b) Which two foods give the least energy?
c) Which foods would you take with you on a long walk in the mountains?
d) Which foods would make a good meal for someone who wants to lose weight?
e) How much energy would you get from 1 gram of bread?
f) How much energy would you get from 2 grams of carrot?

4 In your investigation, did all the energy from the peanut go to the water?
Was it a fair test?
What could you do to improve your investigation?

Things to do

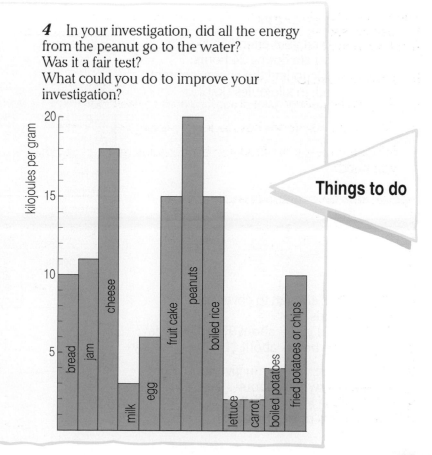

Are you getting enough energy?

Think of the ways in which your body uses up energy.

▶ Make a list of things you have done today which have used up some of your energy.

Energy intake

Sue is a 12-year-old girl. The average energy needed by a girl her age is 9700 kJ per day.

▶ Look at Sue's meals for the last 24 hours and answer these questions.

a Work out Sue's total energy intake for the day (in kJ).

b Did Sue get enough energy for a girl of her age?

c Which 5 foods gave her most energy?

d What do you think would happen if her energy intake was much lower than 9700 kJ per day? How would this make her feel when she needed to be active?

Sue's food	Energy in kJ
cereal	400
milk	600
choc. bar	1500
cheese sandwich	1800
crisps	600
lemonade	700
pizza	1200
chips	1000
apple pie	1200
custard	600
cup of tea	200

How much energy?

▶ Now work out your energy intake for the food you ate during 24 hours.
Use this table to find the energy content of each food, in kilojoules (kJ).

Average portion	kJ	Average portion	kJ	Average portion	kJ
red meat	2000	cornflakes	400	apple	200
chicken	900	milk (1 cup)	600	apple pie	1200
beefburger	1700	yoghurt	400	banana	300
lamb curry	1200	cheese	900	orange	200
pizza	1200	peas	300	chapatti	900
sausages	1500	tomatoes	100	bread (1 slice)	400
fish fingers	700	cabbage	80	pat of butter	200
spaghetti	500	carrots	80	jam	400
rice (boiled)	500	lettuce	40	cake (1 slice)	700
potatoes, boiled	400	choc. bar	1500	cola	600
chips	1000	ice cream	500	coffee	100
baked beans	400	crisps	600	sugar (teaspoon)	100
egg, boiled	400	jelly	300	squash	300
fried	500	biscuit	400	thick soup	600

e Did you eat enough to cover your energy needs?
(12-year-old girl = about 9700 kJ per day;
12-year-old boy = about 11 700 kJ per day)

f What advice would you give someone who is overweight about:
i) taking in less energy?
ii) using up more energy?

Different energy needs

The amount of energy that you need
depends on:

- how big you are,
- how active you are,
- how fast you are growing.

▶ Look at the pictures and then answer
these questions:

g Why do you think that males usually
need more energy than females?

h Why do manual workers need more
energy than office workers? How
much more energy?

i Why does a 13-year-old boy need more
energy than a male office worker?
How much more does he need?

j Why does pregnancy increase a
woman's energy needs?

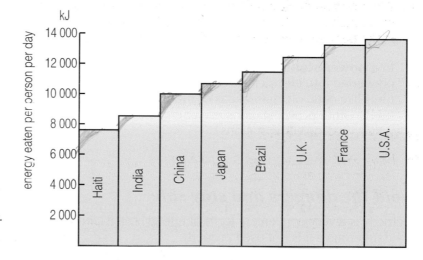

boy 12–15 years
11 700 kJ/day

male manual worker
15 000 kJ/day

female office worker
9800 kJ/day

girl 12–15 years
9700 kJ/day

male office worker
11 000 kJ/day

pregnant woman
10 000 kJ/day

Energy intakes in different countries

▶ Look at the bar-chart:

k Which of these countries eats the most
energy foods per person?

l Which country eats the least?

m Why do you think there are such large
differences?
How will this affect the people's health?
Discuss these questions within your group.

kJ

energy eaten per person per day

14 000 — 12 000 — 10 000 — 8 000 — 6 000 — 4 000 — 2 000

Haiti · India · China · Japan · Brazil · U.K. · France · U.S.A.

---

1 Draw a bar-chart to show the energy
needed per minute for these activities:

sleeping	4 kJ per minute
eating	6 kJ per minute
writing	7 kJ per minute
walking	15 kJ per minute
climbing stairs	20 kJ per minute
running	30 kJ per minute

2 Use the data in the table on the opposite
page to plan:
a) a meal to give you about 3500 kJ
b) a day's diet for a female office worker
who wants to lose weight
c) a day's diet for a male distance-runner
in training for a race.

3 Make a survey of your class to find out
what they eat for lunch.
Can you see any pattern in your results?

4 Find out about the dangers of slimming
too much. What are **anorexia** and **bulimia**?

5 Plan an investigation to find out
which foods birds prefer.

6 Use the internet or your school intranet to
search for information about "world energy
consumption" or "world energy resources".
Write a brief report about the most
important piece of information that you find.
Explain why you think it is important.

Things to do

At home with electricity

Electricity is a very convenient form of energy. Lots of things in our homes use electricity.

▶ Imagine that a storm has brought down the power lines leading to your town. You have no electricity for a week. How would this change your life**?**

Electricity from all the power stations in the country passes into the **National Grid**. This is a system of thick overhead power lines that carry electricity from where it is produced to where it is needed.

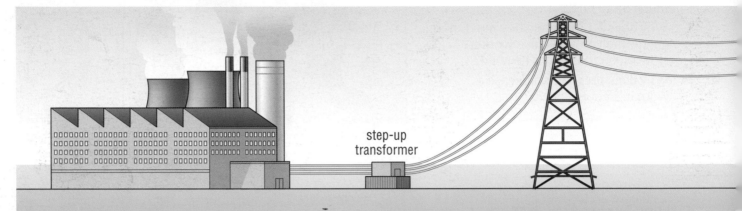

step-up transformer

In a **power station** different forms of energy are converted into electricity. Some power stations use fuels like coal, oil, natural gas or uranium (a nuclear fuel). Other power stations use energy from moving water (hydroelectric stations).

Video 'Generating electricity (1 or 2)

As electricity passes through the National Grid, some energy is lost as heat from the power lines. To keep these energy losses as small as possible the electricity is transformed by a **step-up transformer** so that it has a low current but a very high voltage (400 000 volts).

Avoid the dangers and stay safe

Electricity is a very convenient form of energy, but it can be very dangerous if it is not used properly.

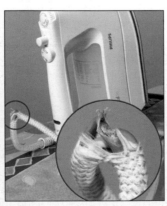

Connecting too many appliances into one socket causes it to heat up.
Why is this dangerous?

When cables become frayed, the insulation wears away and the wires are exposed.
Why is this dangerous?

A light must be switched off before you change the bulb.
Why is it dangerous to change it when it is on**?**

Electricity can travel through water. Why is it dangerous to have a radio connected to the mains sitting on the edge of the bath**?**

Before we can use electricity from the National Grid safely, the voltage must be greatly reduced. In local substations the electricity is transformed by a **step-down transformer** to 230 volts. Underground cables then carry electricity from the substation to our homes.

▶ Where is the nearest substation to your school?

▶ Why is it better to have a National Grid where electricity is shared rather than a system where a power station just provides electricity for the people who live near it?

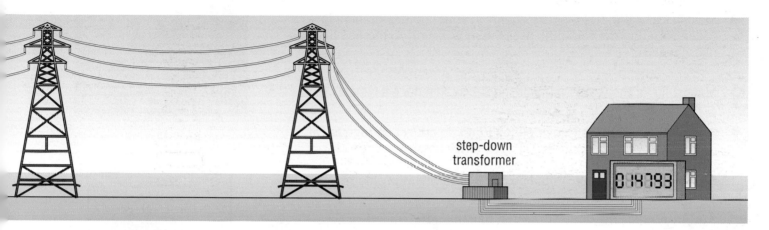

step-down transformer

Reading last time	Reading this time	Tariff	Units	Price of each unit in pence	Amount
		C - Customer reading E - Estimated reading			
Turn over for more information		No code - Company reading			£ p
54590	55500 C	Day	910	7.3400	66.79
12498	13863 C	Night	1365	3.1400	42.86
		Standing charge			14.10
		VAT at 5.00% on charges of £123.75			6.19
		Total amount now due for payment			129.94

All of the electricity used in your home first passes through an **electricity meter**. This measures how many units, or **kilowatt hours (kWh)** of electrical energy you have used. Every 3 months the meter is read and you get a bill from the electricity supply company.

1 Copy and complete:
a) The National Grid carries electricity from ... ... to ... .
b) Electricity passing through the National Grid has a low ... . and a very high ... .
c) The electricity we use in our homes is transformed to ... ... in local ... .

2 Make a survey of how you use electricity in your home.
a) How many lights are there?
b) What electrical appliances do you have that can be plugged into sockets?
c) Do you have anything else that uses electricity, e.g. a cooker, an immersion heater, a shower?

3 Here are the readings from the electricity meter of the Sinclair family at the start and at the end of three months:
27th July 2002   96228
26th October 2002   99762
The cost of electricity is:
10 p per unit for the first 224 units used,
5 p per unit for the remaining units used.
a) How many units of electricity did the family use during the 3 months?
b) How much is their electricity bill for the 3 months?

4 Explain why, inside a bathroom:
a) there should be no electrical sockets.
b) there should be a pull-cord light switch and not a normal wall-mounted switch.

Things to do

Questions

1. Draw Energy Transfer Diagrams for:
   a) a coal fire
   b) putting the rounded stone
   c) an archer pulling back a bow-string and then releasing it.

2. Make a list of 6 things that use energy in your home. Put them in order from the one you think uses the most energy to the one that uses the least.

3. Make a list of the ways that your school could reduce its energy bills.

4. About one-third of all the people on Earth do not get enough to eat.
   a) Why do you think this is? Give as many possible reasons as you can.
   b) What do you think should be done to solve this problem?

5. Advertisements for some HP2 torch batteries claim that they have more energy than others.
   Plan an investigation to find out which of two new batteries has more energy stored.

6. Explain why the following fuels are good for the jobs they do:
   a) sugar in a cup of tea
   b) petrol in a car
   c) gas in a Bunsen burner
   d) wax in a candle
   e) coal in a power station.

7. The energy sources that each country chooses to use depend upon:
   i) economic reasons (price, availability, etc.)
   ii) environmental reasons (pollution, damage to the landscape, etc.)

   Think carefully about these reasons, and then list the advantages and disadvantages for your country, of using:
   a) coal
   b) hydroelectric power
   c) wind power

8. Write about all the energy transfers you can see in the photograph.

The variety of life

3

Have you ever been to the seashore?
It's an interesting and exciting place to visit.

Many creatures live there, especially in rock-pools.
Rock-pools are left behind when the tide goes out.
Each is like a small aquarium. Many plants and animals
survive in rock-pools until the tide returns.

Next time you go to the seashore, have a look to see how
many animals and plants you can find.
But be sure not to damage them. Leave them
undisturbed so that other people can look at them.

oyster catcher

coral weed

mussels

enteromorpha weed

toothed wrack

sea urchin

goby

limpets

shore crab

prawn

hermit crab

whelk

winkle

sea anemones

barnacles

ragworm

starfish

In this topic:
	3a	*Alive or not?*
	3b	*Putting living things into groups*
	3c	*On safari!*
	3d	*It's a green world*
	3e	*Life's building blocks*
	3f	*Find the key*
	3g	*Getting animals ORGANised!*
	3h	*Getting plants ORGANised!*

Alive or not?

How can you tell if something is alive or not**?**

▶ Write down as many ideas as you can about what **all** living things do.
Discuss whether your ideas are true for each of the following:
- rabbit
- table
- tree
- robot
- cheese

▶ The table below shows some more ideas about being alive.
The non-living thing in the table is a car engine.
The living thing can be an animal of your choice.
It could be you!

Draw the table and answer the questions.
The first one is done for you

	Animal (living)	Car engine (non-living)
Does it need air?	yes	yes
Does it move?		
Can it grow?		
Does it need food (fuel)?		
Can it feed on its own?		
Does it give out waste?		
Can it feel things?		
Will it die when it is old?		
Can it be a parent?		
Can it be eaten by another living thing?		

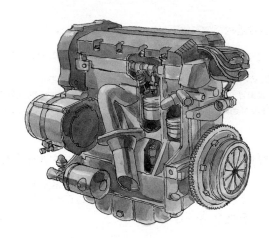

Energy matters

In the previous topic you found that to stay alive living things need energy. Can you remember where living things get their energy from**?**

Sugar is a food that gives us a lot of energy.
Sugar is broken down inside animals and plants to get the energy out
We call this **respiration**.

SUGAR + OXYGEN = CARBON DIOXIDE + WATER + ENERGY FOR LIFE

Oxygen is needed for respiration to take place.
When sugar burns in oxygen it releases energy.
What else do you think is produced**?**

Dear Scientists,

One of our expeditions has found something interesting in Death Valley. They are not sure, but they may have found some very rare seeds. We want to know whether they are alive or not?

Please plan and carry out an investigation to find out if the seeds are living or not. Remember to make it a fair test and send me your report.

Thanks *Des Covery*

Plants: the green machines

Do you know what plants can do that most other living things can't?

They can make their own food by a process called **photosynthesis**. In their leaves they have a green substance called **chlorophyll**. With this they can use energy from sunlight to make sugars.

Differences between plants and animals

▶ Copy and complete this table to show the main differences between these 2 types of living things.

Plants	Animals
1. Don't move around much	1. Move around a lot
2.	2.

Things to do

1 There are some robots that can move and that are sensitive to such things as smells and sounds.
Why do we say they are not alive?

2 Do you know of any plants that provide food for humans as a result of photosynthesis? Make a list and say which part of the plant you think is eaten, e.g. root, leaf, seed, etc.

3 Copy out the activities listed in the left-hand column, then match each with the correct example from the right-hand column:

GROWING	escaping from danger
RESPIRING	becoming a parent
GETTING RID OF WASTE	increasing your body size
MOVING	smelling food
REPRODUCING	having a snack
FEEDING	going to the loo
USING SENSES	using up energy in a race

Putting living things into groups

There are millions of different kinds of plants and animals in the world.

▶ Make a list of 10 animals by yourself.

Compare your list with others in your group.

Each different kind of plant and animal is called a **species**. You have listed 10 species of animal.

Over the years scientists have tried to give every species of plant and animal a name of its own.

▶ Why do you think this has been difficult?

It has been made easier by putting similar living things into groups
This is called **classification**.

▶ The 2 biggest groups are plants and animals. What decides whether a living thing is a plant or an animal?

To make it even easier to identify living things we break the big groups into smaller groups.

```
                              Vertebrates
                           ↗ (have backbones)
                  Animals ↗
                           ↘ Invertebrates
Living    ↗                   (no backbones)
things                     ↗ Flowering
          ↘ Plants       ↗
                           ↘ Non-flowering
```

▶ Which of the groups in the diagram above do you belong to?

▶ How many vertebrates can your group name in one minute?

Invertebrates (animals without backbones)

Jellyfish and sea anemones Jelly-like body. Have tentacles with stinging cells to catch food

Flatworms Flattened body with no segments

Roundworms Long thin body with no segments

Segmented worms Long, tube-shaped body made of segments

Molluscs Many have a shell. Body not in segments. Move around on a muscular foot

Starfish and sea urchin 5 'arms' or star-shaped pattern on their bodies. Spiny skins

Arthropods Jointed legs. Body has hard outer skeleton

The arthropods are a group of invertebrates with jointed legs. They can be divided into 4 smaller groups:

Arthropods

Crustaceans ('cru-stations') Chalky outer skeleton. Most live in water

Insects 6 legs. 3 parts to the body. Have wings

Spiders 8 legs. 2 parts to the body. No wings

Centipedes and millipedes Long body made up of segments. Many legs

▶ Look back at the picture of the rock-pool at the start of this topic.

a There are many invertebrates in the picture. Use the information on the previous page to decide which group each belongs to.

b The goby and the oystercatcher are vertebrates. To which group do you think each belongs?

Vertebrates (all these have a backbone)

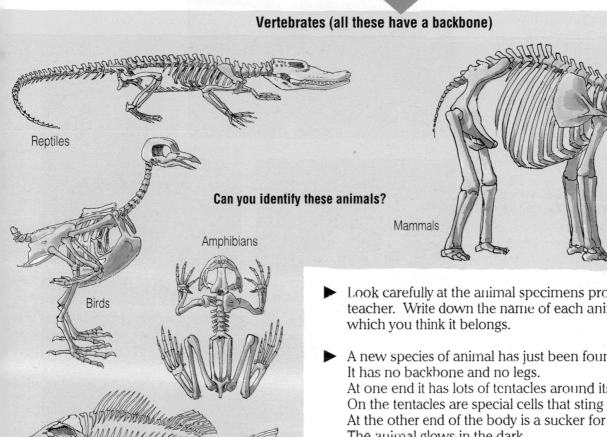

Reptiles

Can you identify these animals?

Amphibians

Birds

Mammals

Fish

▶ Look carefully at the animal specimens provided by your teacher. Write down the name of each animal and the group to which you think it belongs.

▶ A new species of animal has just been found in the deep sea. It has no backbone and no legs. At one end it has lots of tentacles around its mouth. On the tentacles are special cells that sting its prey. At the other end of the body is a sucker for sticking it to rocks. The animal glows in the dark.

Which group do you think the animal belongs to?

Draw a picture of it.

▶ Choose one invertebrate group. Make up an animal that could belong to the group and draw it. Get your friend to try to identify your invented animal.

1 Copy and complete:
Animals with a backbone are called . . . .
Animals that do not have a backbone are called . . . . Invertebrates with jointed legs are put into the group called . . . . This can be divided into four smaller groups called crustaceans, ... , ... and . . . . and . . . .

2 Which animal group has
a) a muscular foot?　c) 8 legs?
b) 6 legs?

3 For each of the following, choose the odd one out and try to give your reason in each case:
a) daisy, flatworm, sea urchin, butterfly
b) fly, spider, ladybird, beetle
c) snail, slug, sea anemone
d) leech, millipede, earthworm

Things to do

On safari!

Hi, my name's Lizzie. Last Saturday I went to the Wildlife park with my friend Richard. We saw llamas with their young. It was a hot day to have such hairy coats. Next we saw a family of baboons. They were very hairy and one mother was feeding its baby. I remembered that **mammals** feed their young on milk. In a different part of the park we saw zebras and camels.

After a stop for drinks at the cafe, we walked to the **reptile** house. There were lizards and snakes from many different countries. We were able to hold the boa constrictor and we could feel its dry skin covered with scales.

We also saw some frogs, toads and salamanders. These had smooth, moist skin and a label said that they were called **amphibians**.

We went to the **bird** house next.
Here there were some very rare birds.
We saw California condors and whooping cranes.
They are in danger because the places where they live are being destroyed.
A bee-eater had beautiful feathers.

We couldn't leave before seeing the aquarium.
There were many types of **fish** in freshwater and seawater tanks.
There were perch and roach as well as tunny, wrasse and bream.
They all had scaly skin and fins for swimming.

On the way home Richard and I talked about the animals that we had seen. Later that day I opened my science book at the page 'Vertebrates: animals with backbones'.

VERTEBRATES : ANIMALS WITH BACKBONES

MAMMALS
Have hair or fur
Feed young on milk
Give birth to live young

BIRDS
Have feathers and wings
Most can fly
Lay eggs with hard shells

REPTILES
Have dry, scaly skin
Lay eggs with soft shells

AMPHIBIANS
Have smooth, moist skin
Breed in water

FISH
Live all of the time in water
Swim using fins
Breathe using gills
Have scaly skin

▶ Copy out this table:

Mammals	Birds	Reptiles	Amphibians	Fish
Llamas				

Read through the story and write down the name of each animal mentioned in the correct column of your table.

▶ Write down 3 reasons why you think vertebrates need a skeleton.

It's a fact!

Archaeopteryx was an early type of bird living 150 million years ago. The fossil remains show that it had feathers (like birds) but also teeth (like reptiles). Draw a picture of what you think the bird looked like.

Things to do

1 Copy and complete:
All vertebrates belong to one of five main groups. The . . . . live in water all the time, breathe using . . . . and swim using . . . .
The . . . . live part of their life on land but go to water to . . . . The . . . . have scaly skin and live all their life on land. . . . . are the only group of vertebrates that can fly. They have . . . . and . . . . to do this. . . . . have fur or . . . . and feed their young on . . . .

2 Which group do you think you belong to? Give your reasons.

3 Find out the names of 2 examples of each of the 5 main vertebrate groups that live wild in Britain.

4 A penguin and an osprey look very different. Write down 3 reasons why scientists think they belong to the same group.

5 In what ways do you think reptiles are better than amphibians at living on land?

It's a green world

What are plants? You already know that they are very different from animals. For one thing they make their own food.

For this reason, plants are often known as **producers** of food, whilst animals are **consumers** of food.

As with animals, you can put plants into groups to help you find their names.

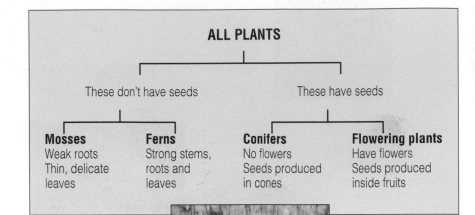

ALL PLANTS

These don't have seeds		These have seeds	
Mosses	**Ferns**	**Conifers**	**Flowering plants**
Weak roots	Strong stems,	No flowers	Have flowers
Thin, delicate	roots and	Seeds produced	Seeds produced
leaves	leaves	in cones	inside fruits

Mosses

- Live in damp places.
- Have thin leaves that easily lose water.
- Make tiny **spores** instead of seeds. These are carried away by the wind. Moss spores grow into new moss plants.

▶ Look at the picture or some moss plants:

a Where do you think the spores are made?

b How heavy do you think the spores will be? Give your reasons.

c Why do you think that mosses are only found in damp places?

Ferns

- Have strong stems, roots and leaves.
- Make spores instead of seeds.
- Have tubes that carry water around inside the plant. The tubes are called **xylem**.

▶ Look at a fern leaf:

d Where do you think the spores are made?

e How are they protected from the rain?

Conifers

- Many are evergreen with leaves like needles.
- Have xylem tubes.
- Their seeds are produced inside **cones**.

▶ Look at a pine cone. Can you find the seeds inside it?

f How do you think these seeds are carried away?

Flowering plants

- Produce flowers.
- Have xylem tubes.
- Make **seeds** inside fruits and berries.

▶ Try cutting open a broad bean seed or maize seed.
Look for a **very young plant** and its **food store** surrounded by a **hard seed coat**.

g Write down your ideas about what each of these parts do.

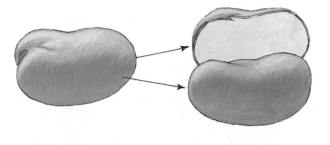

It's a fact!

The largest living plants are the giant redwoods of North America that grow over 100 metres high.

Investigating water loss from leaves

Most flowering plants live on the land. Their leaves often lose water, just as we lose water from our skin as sweat.

Plan an investigation to find out which sort of leaf is best at keeping water. Choose 2 different types of leaf.

Remember that your tests must be fair.

How will you record your results?

Show your plan to your teacher.

Do your investigation and write your report.

1 Copy out and complete the following table.

Group	Do they have strong stems, roots and leaves?	Seeds or spores?	Flowers or not?
mosses ferns conifers flowering plants			

Things to do

2 Write down some examples of how plants have become important as each of the following:
a) food
b) fuel
c) medicine
d) building materials.

3 Over three million years ago, in what was known as the Carboniferous age, vast forests covered the Earth. The plants were similar to the ones in this photograph. They had stems, roots and leaves. These plants reproduced by means of spores. Which group of plants do they belong to?

Life's building blocks

What is a cell?

About 300 years ago Robert Hooke looked down his microscope at a thin layer of cork. He was able to see and draw what looked like tiny rooms. He called them '**cells**'.

With the help of a microscope you too will be able to see cells.

All living things are made up of cells. Some living things are made up of just one cell, but most are made up of many cells.

How big is a cell?

▶ Look at this photograph of human cheek cells:
The cells are 1000 times larger than in real life.

Plan how you could work out the actual size of one of the cells in the photograph. Then work it out.

It's a fact!

Your body probably contains about a million million cells!

cell membrane: contains the cell and controls what passes in and out of the cell

nucleus: controls the cell and contains instructions to make more cells

cytoplasm: where the chemical reactions of the cell take place to keep the cell alive

Looking at plant cells

Make a slide of a thin piece of onion skin.

Look at it under the microscope at low power. What do you see?

Now look at the cells under the microscope at high magnification.

Your onion cells look different from the cheek cells shown above.

All plant cells have:

- a box-like shape
- a thick **cell wall** around the outside to support the cell
- a **vacuole** containing a watery solution called **cell sap**.

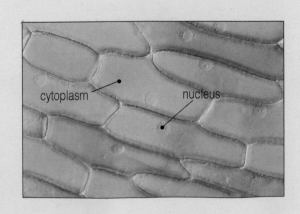

cytoplasm

nucleus

Looking at chloroplasts

Chloroplasts are very small structures that are found in many plant cells. They trap light energy during photosynthesis.

The energy helps plants to make their own food.

Why are there no chloroplasts in your onion cells?

Make a slide of a moss leaf.

Look at the cells under the microscope at high magnification. Can you see the chloroplasts?

Make a large drawing of 2 or 3 cells. Label the parts.

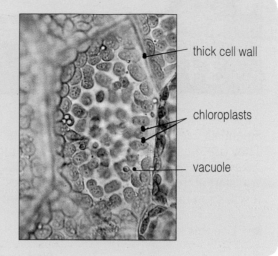

thick cell wall

chloroplasts

vacuole

Special cells

Lots of cells in plants and animals have changed their shape to do a particular job.

Look at these cells:

▶ In the table below the shapes of these cells and the jobs that they do are all jumbled up.

Copy out the table putting in the correct shape and job for each cell.

Type of cell	Shape	Job
sperm cell	hollow tube	carries oxygen
xylem cell	wire-like	swims to the egg
red blood cell	has a tail	carries water
nerve cell	flat disc	carries messages

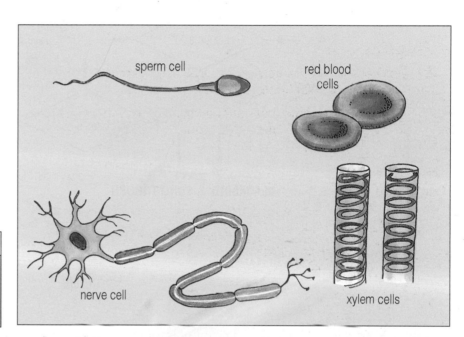

sperm cell

red blood cells

nerve cell

xylem cells

Things to do

1 Copy and complete this table.

	Cheek cell (animal)	Onion cell (plant)	Moss leaf cell (plant)
Does it have a nucleus?			
Does it have a cell wall?			
Does it have chloroplasts?			
Does it have a vacuole?			

2 Write down what you think each of the following cell parts do:
a) chloroplast
b) cell membrane
c) cell wall
d) nucleus.

3 Label the parts on the diagram of the microscope provided by your teacher. Can you remember how you used the microscope? Write down what each of the different parts is used for.

Find the key

Scientists use **keys** to identify living things.
They use these to **classify** living things into groups.
A key has a number of questions.
You start at the beginning and answer "yes" or "no" to each question.
It will soon take you to the animal or plant you want.

▶ Use this key to identify these birds:

Start here

Is it black?

Yes ← → No

Is it speckled?

Yes ← → No

Has it got a
spotted breast?

Yes ← → No

STARLING **BLACKBIRD** **SONG THRUSH**

Has it got
a red breast?

Yes ← → No

ROBIN **SPARROW**

Use the next key to identify 5 small animals found in grassland.
It is set out differently from the first key, but works in the same way.
Start at the beginning and answer the question at each stage.

1	Has legs	Go to 2
	Has no legs	Snail
2	Has 3 or 4 pairs of legs	Go to 3
	Has more than 3 or 4 pairs of legs	Centipede
3	Has 3 pairs of legs	Go to 4
	Has 4 pairs of legs	Spider
4	Has spots on body	Ladybird
	Has no spots on body	Ground beetle

Leaf it out!

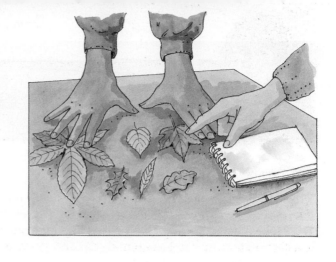

Now try making a key of your own.

1 Put the 6 leaves out in front of you.

2 Think of a question that divides them into 2 groups. Write the question down.

3 Now think up questions to divide each group into two. Write these down.

4 Carry on until you come to each leaf.

5 Write your key out neatly and then try it out on a friend.

▶ Now try making a key of these pond animals.
Do they have legs or not? What are their body shapes like?
Remember to split them up using one question at a time.

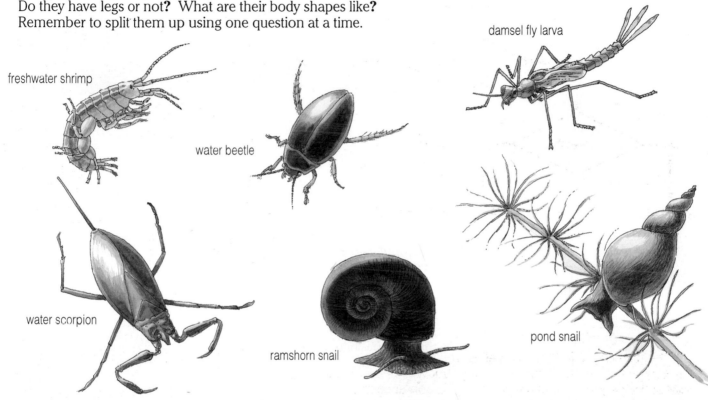

freshwater shrimp

water beetle

damsel fly larva

water scorpion

ramshorn snail

pond snail

Keys are good fun and get easier to use with practice.
Your teacher can give you more keys to try out.

---

1 We can classify plants and animals into groups. Write down:
a) the 4 main groups that make up the plant kingdom
b) the 5 main vertebrate groups
c) any 6 groups of invertebrates.

2 Write down the features that would enable you to classify a fish, an amphibian, a reptile, a bird and a mammal.
Now make a key that you could use to identify each of these vertebrate groups.

3 Write down some features of each of the 4 main groups of plants.
Make a key, using these features, that you could use to identify each group of plants.

4 In the 18th century, Carl Linnaeus worked out a way of naming all living things. He gave them 2 names (called a **genus** and a **species**). His name for you is *Homo sapiens*. Find out what you can about Carl Linnaeus using ROMs, the internet and books.

Things to do

3g Getting animals ORGANised!

Do you know what **organs** are**?**

They are parts of your body that do a particular job for you.

▶ Make a list of some of the organs in your body and say what they do.

Organs are made up of **tissues**.
Tissues are made up of cells that are alike and do the same job.
The tissue in your muscles is made up of identical muscle cells.

  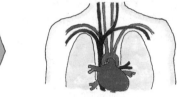

Cells:
The building blocks.

Muscle cells contract and relax.

Tissue:
Similar cells working together in the same way.

Muscle tissue is made of muscle cells that contract and relax together.

Organ:
Groups of tissues working together.

Your heart is made up of muscle tissue. It pumps blood around your body.

System:
A group of organs working together.

Heart and blood vessels make up your **circulatory** system. The circulatory system carries blood around your body.

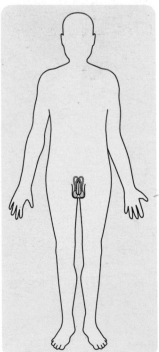

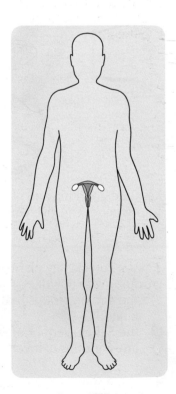

Our ability to produce children depends on our **reproductive system**. The reproductive system of males and females is different.
In the male, sperm is made in the testes and passes out through the penis.
In the female, eggs are made in the ovaries and pass down into the womb where they may develop if fertilisation has taken place.

The systems described in this lesson are only some of the systems of organs to be found in our bodies. Here are the names of some other systems:
a) the nervous system
b) the endocrine system
c) the lymphatic system.

▶ Find out what you can about each of these systems. Find out the names of some of the organs and what job each system does in the body.

It's a fact!

Most animals and plants have many different types of cells all doing different jobs. Your body has over 200 different types of cell!

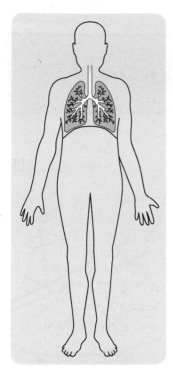
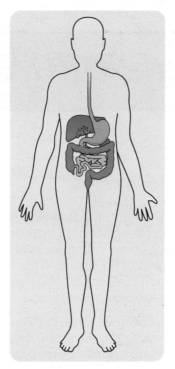
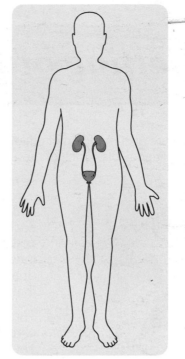
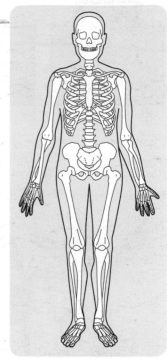

The lungs and windpipe make up your **respiratory system**. The respiratory system enables oxygen to pass from the air into the blood, and carbon dioxide and water vapour to pass from the blood into the air.

The gullet, stomach and intestines make up your **digestive system**. The digestive system breaks down the food that we eat so that important substances can be absorbed by the body.

The kidneys and bladder make up your **excretory system**. The excretory system removes waste substances from your body. These waste substances are removed from your blood by your kidneys and stored as urine in your bladder.

The bones in your body make up your **skeleton**. The skeleton supports all of the organs of your body and protects some of them from damage. Many bones act as levers so that we can move about and carry out important processes like breathing and chewing.

1 Copy and complete:
a) A group of organs working together is called a . . . .
b) A group of tissues working together is called an . . . .
c) A group similar cells working together is called a . . . .

2 Write down the letters A to J. Study the diagram opposite and match each letter with one of the following parts of the body

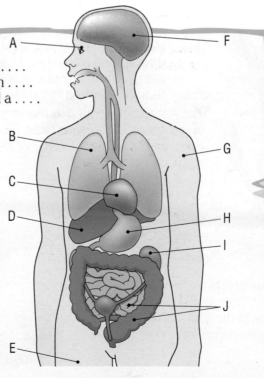

| heart | eye | lungs | stomach | arm |
| liver | intestines | kidney | brain | leg |

3 To which system do each of the following organs belong?
a) Heart   e) Ovary
b) Kidney   f) Stomach
c) Lung   g) Testis
d) Spine

Things to do

3h

Plants have bodies too. They are also made up of different organs, such as flowers, leaves and roots. Each of these organs has a different job to do.

In flowering plants the **flower** is the organ of reproduction. Each flower contains both male and female parts. During pollination, pollen (the male sex cells) is transferred from the male part of the flower to the female part of the same or a different flower. The fruit that forms contains seeds that will grow into new plants.

The seeds of some plants, like peas, beans and sweet corn, contain large amounts of carbohydrates.
They are good to eat because they give us energy.

The **leaves** of a plant are where all of the plant's food is made. They contain a green pigment called **chlorophyll** which traps energy from sunlight and uses it to turn carbon dioxide and water into carbohydrates like starch and sugar.
This process is called **photosynthesis**.

The **roots** of a plant absorb water from the soil. This water often contains soluble nutrients like nitrates that are essential for the plant to grow. This solution passes through the plant stem to all of the leaves. The nutrients are used and any unwanted water is lost into the air though pores on the surface of the leaves.

► Luckily for us, some plants make a lot more food than they use. They store this extra food in the plant stem or in the roots. Can you identify all of these root vegetables**?**

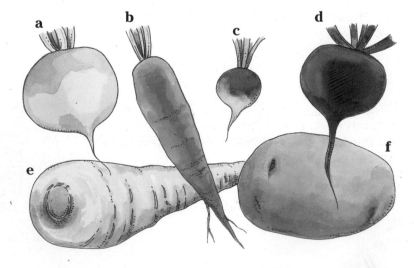

40

Lots of plants don't produce flowers but that doesn't mean that they don't reproduce. It's simply that they do it in different ways.

For example, mosses reproduce from spores that form inside a capsule. Once the capsule is ripe the spores are released onto the ground. Each spore can develop into a new plant. Can you see the capsules on the moss plant?

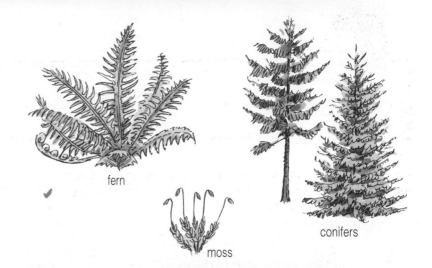

fern

moss

conifers

Investigation: Beet this!

A beetroot is a plant organ that stores food over the winter. In the spring the new plant uses this food for growth. Beetroot tissue is made up of cells that contain a red dye. This dye leaks out if the cells are put into hot water.

How can you get the most dye out of a chip of beetroot?

Plan your investigation.

Decide what apparatus you will need and how you are going to record your results.

Remember that it must be a fair test.

Show your plan to your teacher and then start your investigation.

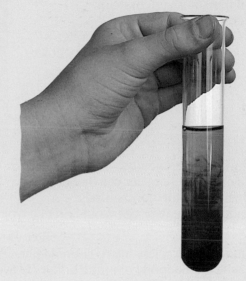

Things to do

1 Copy and complete:
On a plant
a) the job of a flower is to make . . . .
b) the job of a leaf is to make . . . .
c) the job of a root is to absorb . . . . containing . . . .

2 Write down the letters A to F. Study this diagram and match each letter with one of the following parts of the plant:

| root | leaf | fruit | flower | bud | stem |

3 Imagine that you are a particular organ in a plant. Write about what you are like and what job you do in the plant. Don't forget to say why you think that you are so important.

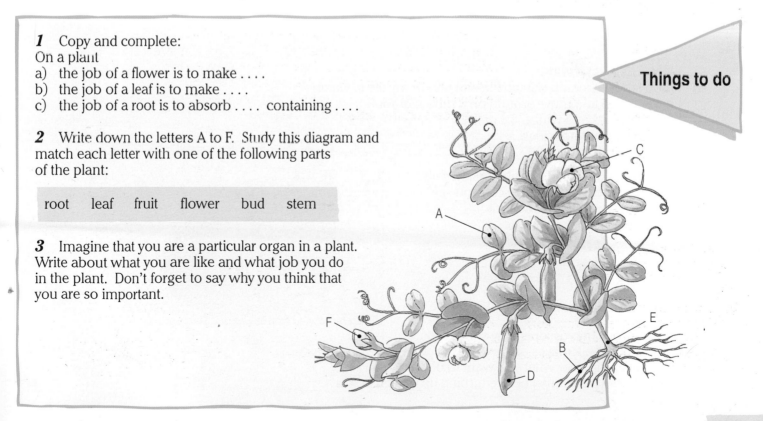

Questions

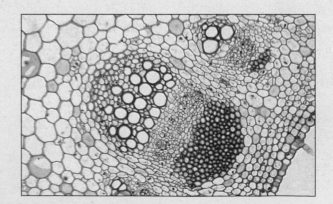

1. A visitor from outer space lands on Earth.
The first thing that it sees is a steam train passing by.
Give 2 reasons why the visitor thinks it is alive.
Give 2 reasons why you think the visitor is wrong.

2. Look at this photograph of an animal:
Do you think it is vertebrate or
an invertebrate?
Which group do you think it belongs to?
Write down your reasons for your choice.

3. Cells can do different jobs.
Draw a cartoon character cell that does a
particular job in the human body.
Write about what your cell would do in a typical day.

4. Try putting some celery into coloured water. You can colour the
water with a little food colouring or ink. Leave your celery for a few
hours and then look at it. The coloured lines are xylem.
What job do you think xylem does?
Which plant groups have xylem and which do not?

5. Who am I?
   a) I have 6 legs, and wings.
   b) I have smooth, damp skin and spend part of my life in water.
   c) I have a shell and move around on a muscular foot.
   d) I have feathers and wings. I can fly!
   e) I have 8 legs but no wings.

6. Look carefully at this photograph of plant cells.
How many different types of cell can you see?
Describe or draw each different cell.
Why don't they all look the same?

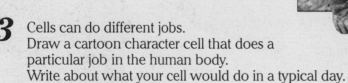

7. When using your microscope, why should you:
   a) never touch the surfaces of the lenses or mirror?
   b) put a cover slip over what you want to observe on a slide?
   c) focus on low power first before turning up to high power?

Forces

4

Your life is full of forces.

Everything that you do needs a force.
To lift your pen needs a force.
To turn the page needs a force

In the photo, the people are being pulled down the slide by the force of gravity. And they are being slowed by another force – the force of friction.

In this topic you can investigate forces, to find out what they can do and how to measure them.

Using forces

push

All these people are using **forces**.

▶ Look at the pictures above and find the force in each one.

a Write down a list of words that describe the forces in the pictures. Your first word can be *push*.

b Write down 5 things that you have done today using a force. Which muscles did you use?

Force-meters

▶ Look at diagrams 1 to 4, of some **force-meters**: They are sometimes called newton-meters or spring-balances.

Each one is measuring the size of a force. We measure the size of a force in **newtons** (also written as **N**).

c For each force-meter, write down the largest force that it can measure on its scale.

d What force is each one showing on its scale here?

e The apple is pulling down with a force called its **weight**. What is the weight of the apple?

The weight of this book is about 5 newtons.

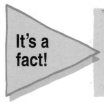

It's a fact! An ant can pull with a force of $\frac{1}{1000}$ newton, a family car can push with 5000 newtons, and a moon-rocket exerts 30 million N.

Measuring forces

This table lists some jobs that need a force:

Copy out the table.

In each case, first make a **prediction** of how big you think the force will be. Write it down.

Then **measure** that force with a force-meter. Take care to choose the right force-meter for each job.

	Size of force in newtons	
	Prediction	Actual
Lift a bag	20 ?	
Pull a stool along the floor		
Pull the stool more quickly		
Weigh a Bunsen burner	—	
Stretch a rubber-band to twice its length		
Open a door		

Finger strength

Plan an investigation to find the strength of people's finger muscles.

You can use bathroom scales as shown, and test several different people.

- How will you make sure it is a fair test?
- How will you record your results?
- How can you make your results more reliable?

Ask your teacher to check your plan, and then do your investigation.

Is there any pattern in your results?

1 Copy and complete:
Forces can do 3 things. They can:
a) change the **size** or **shape** of an object (for example: squeezing a sponge)
b) change the speed of an object to make it move **faster** (for example: kicking a ball) or to make it move . . . . (for example: catching a ball)
c) change the **direction** of a moving object (e.g. a ball bouncing off a . . . .).

2 Sketch 3 of the pictures at the top of the opposite page and mark with an arrow where you think a force is acting.
For example:

3 Suppose you are given a ruler, a rubber-band, a paper-clip, some cotton thread and some sellotape. How could you use these to make your own force-meter?
Draw a diagram of your design and label it.

4 The newton is named after Sir Isaac Newton, a famous scientist who lived 300 years ago.

Do some research, and then write 2 paragraphs about him.

Things to do

Friction and other forces

A small push can slide this book along the table. But why does it stop moving?

The book is touching the table, and they are both rough. When they rub together, the force of **friction** slows down the book.

Friction can be useful.
You can't walk unless there is friction between your shoes and the ground.

▶ List 3 other examples where friction is helpful to us.

Friction can be a problem.
If there is too much friction in a bicycle, then it is hard to pedal.

Because of friction some of your energy is used to warm up the moving parts. This is like rubbing your hands together to make them warm.

You can make the friction less by **lubricating** the moving parts with oil or grease.

▶ Look at this photo of a bicycle:
Copy the table and fill in as many examples in each column as you can.

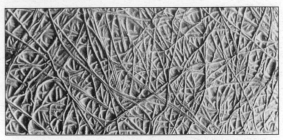

The surface of paper is rough (magnified ×100)

Riding a bicycle	
Friction is needed	Friction is not wanted
tyres on the road	

Friction is a **contact** force. It only happens if things are touching.

Other forces can act at a distance, without touching. Here are 3 examples:

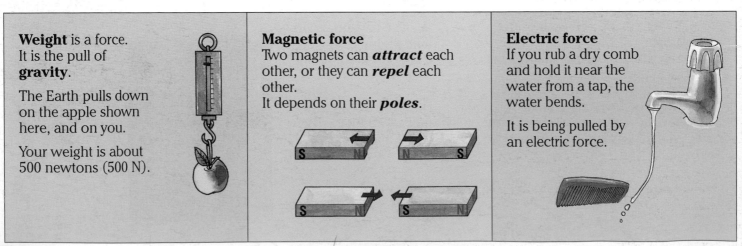

Weight is a force. It is the pull of **gravity**.

The Earth pulls down on the apple shown here, and on you.

Your weight is about 500 newtons (500 N).

Magnetic force
Two magnets can *attract* each other, or they can *repel* each other.
It depends on their *poles*.

Electric force
If you rub a dry comb and hold it near the water from a tap, the water bends.

It is being pulled by an electric force.

Investigating shoes

Imagine you are a shoe designer.
You have been asked to design some shoes
that will have a good 'grip' so that they won't
slide easily.

Here are some things that make a shoe slide
easily or not:

a the type of sole
b the ground surface it is on
c the weight of the person in the shoe.

Choose **one** of these (**a**, **b** or **c**).

***Then find out how changing it makes
the shoe more or less easy to slide.***

- What do you make sure to change and what
  do you need to measure?

- How will you ensure it is a fair test?
  What things (variables) do you need to
  keep the same each time?

- How will you record your results?

Ask your teacher to check your plan, and
then do it.

What pattern do you find?

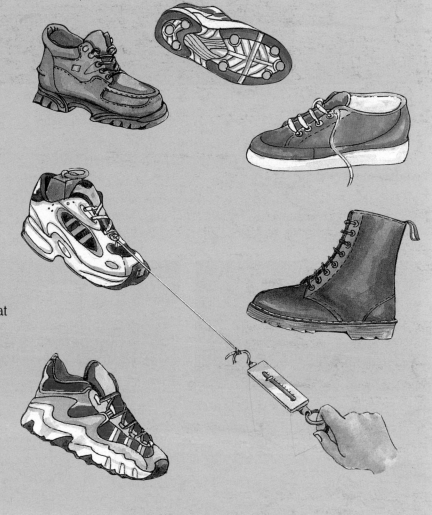

---

1 Copy and complete:
a) Friction is a . . . . which tries to slow
   down objects when they rub together.
b) Friction can be reduced by . . . . the
   moving parts with oil.
c) Weight is a . . . . It is the pull of . . . . by
   the Earth.
d) Two other forces are magnetic . . . . and
   electric . . . .

2 Suppose you wake up tomorrow
morning and find that there is no friction
at all in your home.
Write 2 paragraphs to describe what could
happen to you.

3 How can you reduce the friction in
a bicycle?

4 Why is friction important for road safety?
What can happen if the weather is
a) wet?   b) icy?

5 Make a table as shown:

Friction is needed	Friction is not wanted
catching a ball	swimming

Think about different sports, and list 5
examples in each column.

Things to do

47

Shape is important

Air resistance

We are surrounded by air. When anything moves, the air rubs against it and slows it down. This sort of friction is called **air resistance** (or **drag**).

Air resistance is not a problem when we walk about because we are not moving very quickly. However, it does become a problem if we want to go faster.

▶ Look how the shape of a motor car has changed over the last century. Which shape produces least air resistance?

▶ The modern car has a **streamlined** shape. How does this improve the efficiency of the car?

▶ The racing cyclist needs to reduce air resistance as much as possible so that he will go faster. How is he doing this?

Motor cars and aircraft are designed to be as streamlined as possible using sophisticated computer programs. Scale models are tested in a **wind tunnel**. The smoke allows designers to see how well the air moves over the shape.

Moving through water

In the same way, as objects pass through water there is a friction force that slows them down.

▶ How does the shape of a dolphin help it to move easily through the water?

Swimmers looking to win an Olympic medal take every opportunity to reduce the friction between themselves and the water.
They wear costumes made of special low-resistance material and many of them wear swimming caps.
The few hundredths of a second they save might be the difference between a gold medal and a silver medal.

▶ Some swimmers shave all of the hair from their bodies. How does this improve their times?

What shape passes easiest through liquids?

You can investigate how the **shape** of an object affects how quickly it falls through a liquid.

- Take some pieces of plasticine of similar size and make them into different shapes, like the shape of a cube, a sphere, a pyramid, an egg, a pencil shape and a pancake.
  Predict which shapes will fall fastest, and slowest.

- Fill a long glass tube, like a measuring cylinder, with water. Time how long it takes for each plasticine shape to fall to the bottom of the tube.
  Make a table of your results.
  Which shape falls quickest? Which shape falls slowest?

- Fill the glass tube with another liquid like cooking oil and repeat the test.
  Make a table of your results.
  Do you notice anything different between the times the shapes took to fall through water and through cooking oil?
  Can you explain this?

---

1 Copy and complete:
a) When an object moves through air there is a friction force called . . . .
b) This friction is reduced when the shape of an object is . . . .
c) When the friction between a motor car and the air is reduced, it can go . . . .

2 We sometimes use the word 'thickness' to describe how hard it is to pour a liquid and how easy it is for something to pass through it. For example, golden syrup is very thick; it pours very slowly and is difficult to stir with a spoon.
Design an experiment that would allow you to compare the thickness of some liquids.

3 Explain the following:
a) In what ways is a fish designed to move easily through water?
b) In the past the Navy has carried out experiments involving pouring a kind of oil over the bows (front) of ships so that they move more quickly through the water. How do you think this worked?
c) How is friction between boat and water reduced in a hydrofoil?

4 Draw a design for a streamlined futuristic car. Remember that it has to be comfortable to sit in.

Things to do

Forces at work

Levers

A lever is a simple **machine**. It helps us to do jobs more easily.

▶ The diagram shows two spanners, used for turning a nut on a bolt.

Which spanner would you use to undo a very tight nut? How can you make it even easier to undo the nut?

▶ Look at the door handle in the diagram:
It is a lever. Which is the best place (A, B or C) for you to apply a force? (Try this if you can.)

▶ Design a simple machine or tool that would help an old person to turn a stiff door handle. Draw a diagram and label it.

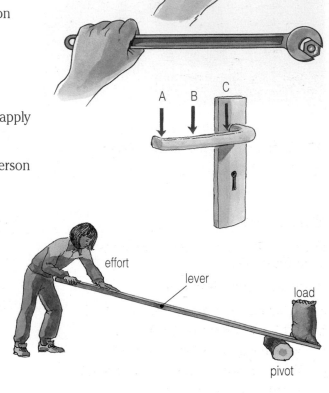

Here is a lever being used to lift a **load** (the sack):
The pivot (or '**fulcrum**') is near the sack.
The girl is applying an **effort** force to turn the lever and lift the load.
In this case, a small effort force can lift a large load.
This lever is a **force-magnifier**.

Sometimes levers are used as **distance-magnifiers**.
The long hand on a clock is a distance-magnifier; a small movement near the centre of the clock becomes a big movement at the end of the pointer.
There are levers in your body that are used like this.
Bend your arm and think about what is happening.

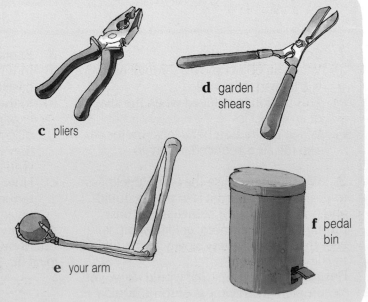

Here are some common machines using levers.
For each one, write down:
- where the pivot is
- where the effort force is applied (by you)
- where the load is
- whether it is a force-magnifier or a distance-magnifier.

c pliers

d garden shears

a wheelbarrow

b opening a paint tin

e your arm

f pedal bin

Pulleys

A **pulley** is another simple machine.

Here are two pulley systems that could be used on a building site:

What are pulley systems useful for?

Investigate these two pulley systems.

You can use a clamp stand to hold up the top pulley. You can use slotted weights for the load. You can measure the effort force with a force-meter (spring-balance).

Measure the effort needed to lift up different loads.

What do you find?

Which pulley system is easier to use?

Ring a bell

The diagram shows a design for a door-bell in an old castle.

When the handle is pulled:

g   What happens to the blue rope?

h   Which way does pulley A turn?

i   Which way does lever B move?

J   Which way does the red rope move?

k   What happens to the bell?

l   Is lever C a force-magnifier or a distance-magnifier?

m   Can you design a simpler system? Draw a diagram of it.

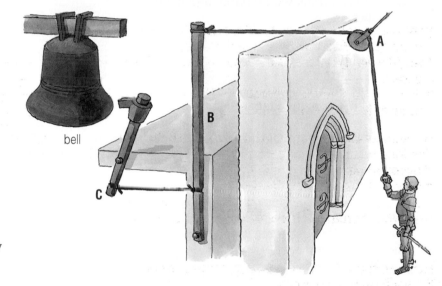

bell

---

1   Copy and complete:
a)   Levers and pulleys are simple . . . .
b)   A lever has a pivot or . . . .
c)   A lever can be a . . . . -magnifier or a . . . . -magnifier.

2   Think about the ways you can move your arms, fingers, legs, jaw, etc.
Make a list of the levers in your body.
For 3 of these levers, draw a simple diagram and show where the pivot is.

3   Design a handle for a bathroom tap to be used by an old person or invalid.

4   Imagine you are using a spanner to undo a tight nut. Copy and complete this Energy Transfer Diagram:

. . . . stored in my body

. . . . energy of the nut as it turns

. . . . warming up the nut (due to friction)

5   Design a system of pulleys and levers that will allow you to open the front door of your house from your bedroom.
Sketch a diagram of your system.

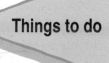

Things to do

Move it!

To move something you have to apply a **force**.

▶ Look at the cartoon:

a Which one needs the bigger force to start moving – the heavy man or the little girl?

> a push force is needed to start moving

Now suppose both sledges are moving across the ice, at the same speed.

b Which one needs a bigger force to stop it?

Objects usually slow down and stop, because of friction (see page 46).

c What happens to the sledge if there is very little friction?

d What do you think would happen to it if there was no friction at all?

We show forces in diagrams by arrows.
The bigger the force, the longer the arrow.

▶ Look at the diagram. It shows a book being pushed across a table.

e Which is the bigger force: the push of the finger or the force of friction?

f Do you think the book is moving? Why?

g How big is the push force in newtons? (Use your ruler to measure it.)

h How big is the friction force?

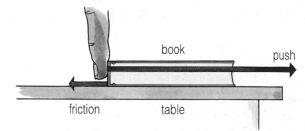

scale: 1 cm stands for 1 newton

The friction force cancels out part of the push force. We are left with a **resultant** force.

i How big is the resultant force here?

j What would be the resultant force if the push force = 3 newtons and the friction force = 2 newtons?

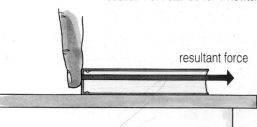

resultant force

It is the resultant force that makes the book move.
The bigger the resultant force, the faster the book moves.

▶ Draw a diagram of the book and show a push force of 2 newtons and a friction force of 2 newtons.

k What is the resultant force?

l Does the book move or stay still?

Isaac Newton wrote a 'law' about these ideas:

If an object has **no** resultant force on it, then

- if it is at rest, it stays at rest (not moving)

- if it is moving, it keeps moving at a steady speed in a straight line.

Investigating movement

Let a toy car roll down a slope:

Plan an investigation to see how the **time taken** by a car to travel down depends on the **height** it starts from.

You can use a pair of *light gates*: As the car passes through the first gate it starts an electrical timer. The timer stops as the car passes the second gate. The computer shows how long it took.

What do you think will happen? Write down your *prediction*.

- Make a list of things you will keep the same, to make it a fair test.
- How far apart will you place the light gates?
- Will you push the car or just let it go?
- How often will you repeat it at each height?
- How will you record your results?

Show your plan to your teacher and then do it.

What did you find out? Does it agree with your prediction?

Now answer these questions. In your answers, try to include some of the words in the box.

weight	pull of gravity
resultant force	friction
potential energy	kinetic energy

m Why does the car move down the ramp?

n What is the name given to the energy that the car has at the top?

o Where did this energy come from?

p What is the name given to the energy it has at the bottom?

q Where is the energy when the car has stopped?

---

1 Copy and complete:
a) An object can have . . . . than one force acting on it.
b) If there is no resultant . . . . on the object, its movement does . . . . change.
c) Newton's law on this says: if an object has no . . . . force on it, then
- if it is at rest then it stays at . . . . (not . . . .)
- if it is moving then it keeps on . . . . at a . . . . speed in a . . . . line.

2 Use a scale of 1 cm for 1 newton to draw force diagrams for:
a) a book being pushed by a force of 6 N with a friction force of 2 N
b) a toy boat weighing 4 N floating on water.

3 Look at the next page and collect a suitable bottle or can, to bring to the next lesson.

Things to do

▶ Look at these diagrams of some rubber-band racers.

Choose **one** of them and then build it.

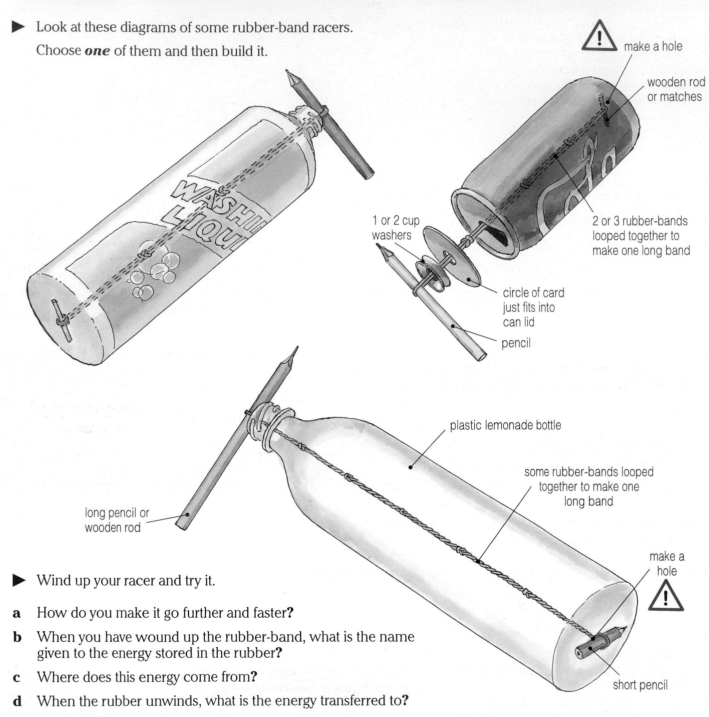

⚠ make a hole

wooden rod or matches

1 or 2 cup washers

2 or 3 rubber-bands looped together to make one long band

circle of card just fits into can lid

pencil

long pencil or wooden rod

plastic lemonade bottle

some rubber-bands looped together to make one long band

make a hole ⚠

short pencil

▶ Wind up your racer and try it.

a How do you make it go further and faster?

b When you have wound up the rubber-band, what is the name given to the energy stored in the rubber?

c Where does this energy come from?

d When the rubber unwinds, what is the energy transferred to?

e If you overwind the rubber-band, your racer will slip and skid on the floor. How can you increase the friction and stop 'wheelspin'?

f Where on your racer do you want to make friction as low as possible? How can you do this?

Investigations with your racer

▶ Choose **one** of these investigations.

Plan it carefully.
Make sure it is a fair test.
When your plan is complete, do the investigation.

1 Investigate how to make your racer travel in a straight line.

Whose racer can travel a straight 3 metre course in the shortest time?

2 Investigate how your racer travels up a hill. How steep can you make the slope?

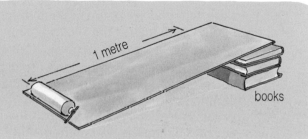

1 metre

books

Whose racer can travel for 1 metre up the steepest slope?

3 Investigate how the speed of your racer depends on the number of turns that you wind it up.

$$\text{average speed} = \frac{\text{distance travelled}}{\text{time taken}}$$

You will need a stop-clock.
You can use the formula shown in the box.

▶ Make a report on what you did and what you found out. It can be a written report or a poster.

▶ If you have time, you can do another one of these investigations.

1 Draw a sketch of your racer and label its important features.
How would you change the design to make it go faster?

2 Explain how your racer works and how you stored energy in it. Use the following words in your explanation:

| food | potential energy | strain energy |
| kinetic energy | friction | lever | resultant force |

3 Copy and complete this Energy Transfer Diagram for your racer:

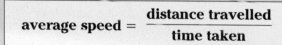

. . . . stored in your body → . . . . stored in the wound-up rubber band → . . . . energy of the racer

. . . . warming up the room

Things to do

Questions

A kingfisher diving into water

1 Streamlining reduces friction.
Give 3 examples of streamlining in animals, and explain how it helps the animals.

2 How is friction reduced in:
a) a hovercraft?
b) a racing car?
c) a yacht?

3 The table tells you about the braking distances for a car going at 15 metres per second (33 m.p.h.):

a) Draw a bar-chart of the data, and label it.
b) What is the best combination of road and tyres for stopping quickly? What is the braking distance in this case?
c) What is the worst combination? How much worse is it than the best combination?
d) Why is it harder to stop on wet roads than on dry roads?

Braking distances		
Dry road	new tyres	13 metres
	old tyres	14 metres
Wet road	new tyres	18 metres
	old tyres	23 metres

4 Plan an investigation to compare the brakes on different bicycles.
How would you make it a *fair* test?
How would you make it a *safe* test?
What measurements would you make?
(Do not do this investigation without adult supervision.)

5 Plan an investigation of a toy sailing boat.
Decide what you would investigate, and how you would make it a fair test.
What features would a good design have?

6 Design a machine to help someone who can't bend their back to pick up a book from the floor.

7 Look at the photograph at the start of this topic.
Design your own slide or chute.
Draw a labelled diagram of it, including any safety features.
Where do you want friction to be:
a) low?   b) high?

8 Write a 'safety checklist' for *either* a pram *or* a bicycle.
It should show what you would check to see if it is safe to use.

Growing up

5

As we grow up, each of us changes from a baby to a child, then to a teenager and eventually to an adult.

But growing up doesn't just mean we get bigger. We also grow up in other ways.

We develop mentally. Our emotions change as we mix with other people. Most of us will find a partner and may have children of our own. Then we will have responsibilities to our partner and to our children.

5a Having babies

▶ Look at the different stages in a human life shown here:

Put them in the correct order starting with the youngest.

Baby talk

Why do people decide to have a baby? Some of the reasons that people give for having children are shown below.

▶ Discuss in groups which you think are good reasons and which are not. Try to put the reasons in order starting with the one you agree with most.

> I want a son to take to football matches.

> People would think that there was something wrong if we didn't have children.

> Bringing up children will be a challenge.

> We just love children.

> Having children will bring us closer together.

> We want to enjoy bringing up a family.

> Children will bring more money into the house.

▶ When do you think is the best time for a couple to have a baby?

When do you think is the wrong time?

What sort of preparations do you think will have to be made before the baby is born?

> Our children will look after us when we are old.

> Our parents would love to have grandchildren.

How are babies made?

To start a baby the male and female sex cells must join together. A **sperm** from a man must join with an **egg** from a woman. This is called **fertilisation**. In humans it occurs inside the woman's body.

Here are the parts of a man that are used for making sperms:

▶ Your teacher will give you a copy of this diagram.

a Shade in blue where sperms are made.

b Shade in red where fluid is added to the sperms.

c Shade in yellow the tubes that the sperms pass through to get to the outside.

d List the parts that the sperms pass through.

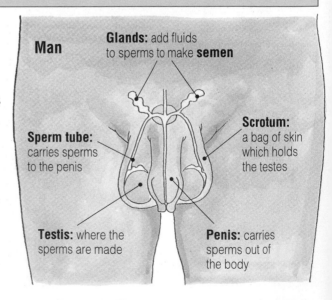

Man

Glands: add fluids to sperms to make **semen**

Sperm tube: carries sperms to the penis

Scrotum: a bag of skin which holds the testes

Testis: where the sperms are made

Penis: carries sperms out of the body

Here are the parts of a woman that are used to make eggs and produce babies:

▶ Your teacher will give you a copy of this diagram.

e Shade in blue where eggs are made.

f Shade in red where fertilisation may take place.

g Shade in yellow where the baby develops.

h List the parts that the egg would pass through on its way out of the body.

Woman

Uterus: in a pregnant woman the baby grows here

Egg tube: carries the egg to the uterus every month

Ovaries: where the eggs are made

Cervix: the opening to the uterus

Vagina: receives the sperm

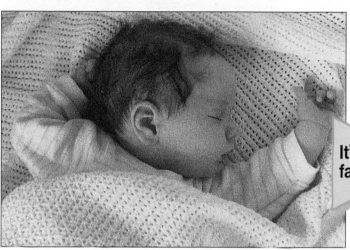

It's a fact!

When a girl is born she has thousands of partly-formed eggs in each ovary. When she grows into a woman an egg will be released from one of her ovaries about every 28 days.

▶ Copy out these sentences and add as much as you can, using words from the box opposite:
- I know that females have …
- I know that males have …
- Fertilisation is when …
- Babies grow …

Now make some sentences of your own using some of these words.

| testes | egg | uterus | sperms |
| vagina | egg tube | sperm tube |
| where eggs are made |
| penis | ovaries | scrotum |
| where sperms are made |

Things to do

1 Copy out the words in the following list. If you think that they are female put (F) after them. If you think that they are male put (M).

ovaries	egg tube	penis
uterus	testes	vagina
scrotum	sperm tube	cervix

2 Sometimes a woman's egg tubes get blocked.
a) Why do you think that a woman with both egg tubes blocked cannot have a baby?
b) Why do you think that a woman with one egg tube blocked might be able to have a baby?

3 Copy out the list of organs on the left and match each organ with its correct job from the list on the right.

penis	carries sperms to penis
ovaries	where the baby grows
sperm tube	makes sperms
vagina	carries eggs to uterus
uterus	makes eggs
testes	receives sperms
egg tube	holds testes
scrotum	carries sperms out of body

Fertilisation

▶ Look at these photographs of the human sperm and the human egg. Write down as many differences as you can between the sperm and the egg.

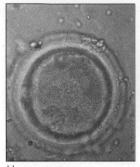
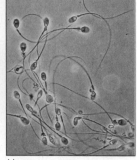

Human egg   Human sperm

Making love

When people 'make love' or 'have sex' it is not just so that they can have babies. Men and women can enjoy making love at other times too. They use it as a way of showing their love for each other. By having sex a man and woman can feel very close to each other. Making love is far more than putting a sperm and an egg together.

When the man feels excited his penis becomes stiff. This erection is due to blood flowing into the penis.

When the woman becomes excited her vagina becomes moist and widens.

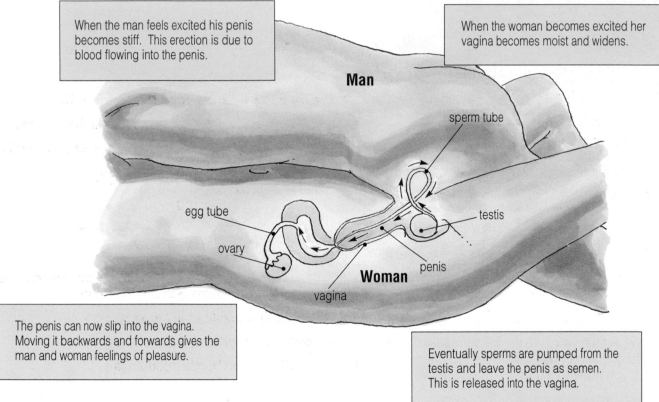

Man

sperm tube

egg tube

ovary

testis

penis

Woman

vagina

The penis can now slip into the vagina. Moving it backwards and forwards gives the man and woman feelings of pleasure.

Eventually sperms are pumped from the testis and leave the penis as semen. This is released into the vagina.

▶ Write out the following statements. Put (T) for true after those you agree with and (F) for false after those you don't agree with.

People have sex because they want babies.

Fertilisation takes place in the egg tube.

You have to be married to have sex.

During sex body fluids are released.

A sperm and an egg are not cells.

For sex to occur a man's penis must be hard.

Some people don't have sex (are virgins) all their life.

It's a fact!

Only about a teaspoonful of semen is released at a time, but this can contain as many as 500 million sperms.

After making love ...

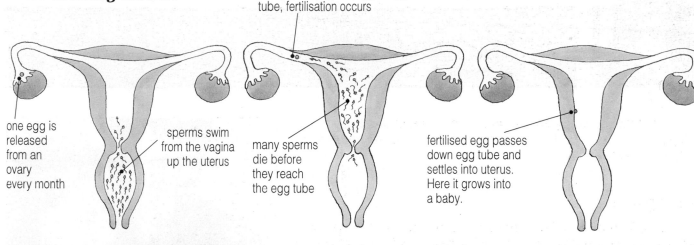

one egg is released from an ovary every month

sperms swim from the vagina up the uterus

if a sperm meets an egg in egg tube, fertilisation occurs

many sperms die before they reach the egg tube

fertilised egg passes down egg tube and settles into uterus. Here it grows into a baby.

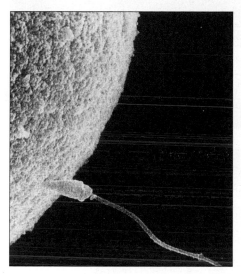

When the sperm meets the egg it loses its tail. The sperm head enters the egg and its nucleus joins with the egg nucleus: this is **fertilisation**.

What do you think?

► In groups discuss these statements:

It is against the law to have sex under the age of 16.

Many people say that they have had sex when they haven't.

People should have sex only if they are in love with each other.

Men are more interested in sex than women.

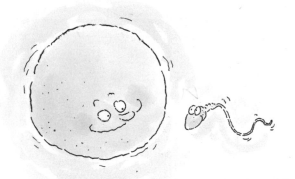

Not too many

► Many societies have their own rules and traditions which help to stop too many children being born. Write about:

- what these rules and traditions are in *your* society
- how they help to control the growth of the population
- rules and traditions used in other countries.

---

1 Copy out and complete the following sentences:
a) Fertilisation is the joining together of . . . .
b) The sperms are released into . . . .
c) To get to the egg tube, the sperms swim . . . .
d) An egg is released from an ovary every . . . .
e) The fertilised egg passes down the egg tube . . . .

2 What do you think might happen if the fertilised egg splits into two?

3 Try to explain each of these statements:
a) Fish and frogs produce thousands of eggs into the water.
b) Humans usually produce one egg at a time inside the body of the woman.
c) Men produce millions of sperms.

Things to do

Ruth and Jim

5c

Ruth and Jim had wanted a baby for a long time. When Ruth missed her period, they hoped she might be **pregnant**. Ruth went to see her doctor and took along a sample of her urine for a test. After a short time she was told that the test was positive – she was pregnant! She told Jim straight away. They were both so happy and excited at the thought of a baby after waiting for so long.

In the weeks that followed they started to make plans for the new baby. Ruth went to the **ante-natal clinic** regularly. The nurse asked her questions like:
Was it her first pregnancy?
Had she ever had any serious illnesses?
Had there been serious illnesses in her family or in Jim's?
Were there any twins in her family or in Jim's?

Whenever Ruth went to the clinic the nurse weighed her and measured her blood pressure. The midwife or doctor examined her on each visit and she was given lots of advice about how to prepare for the birth of her baby.

4 weeks

▶ Think about Ruth's visits to the ante-natal clinic and answer the following questions.

a Why do you think Ruth was asked about serious illnesses in the family?

b Why was she asked if there were twins in the family?

c Why do you think she was weighed?

d Why do you think her blood pressure was taken?

e Ruth doesn't smoke. Why might the nurse have been worried if she did?

7 weeks

A new life begins

When the fertilised egg passed down Ruth's egg tube, it settled in the thick wall of her uterus. As it grew it eventually formed a **fetus** ('feet-us').

▶ Look at these photographs of the developing fetus inside the uterus:

f What changes can you see? Write them down.

Early in pregnancy, a plate-shaped organ called a **placenta** forms in the uterus. This acts as a barrier stopping infections and harmful substances from reaching the fetus. Inside the placenta the blood of the fetus and the mother come close together. The fetus is attached to the placenta by the **cord**.

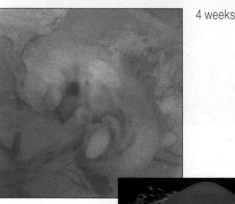

▶ Write down your answers to these questions.

g How do you think food and oxygen get to the fetus?

h How do you think the fetus gets rid of waste?

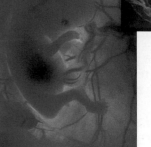

14 weeks

► Look at this diagram of the fetus inside the mother:

i How do you think it is protected during its development?

j Can you see that it is surrounded by a fluid? How do you think this helps the fetus?

Immature thoughts

► Imagine that you are inside the uterus before birth. What is it like?
How do you feed?
How do you breathe?
How are you protected from bumps?
What do you hear?

Write a short story about your experiences.

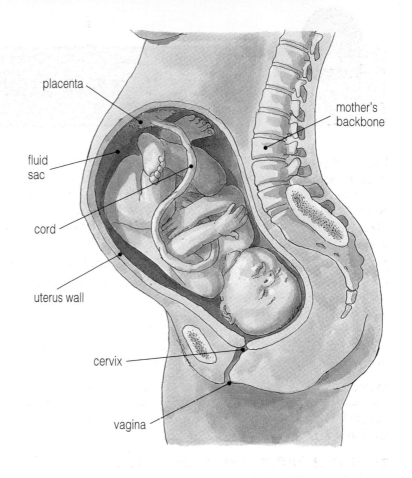

placenta

mother's backbone

fluid sac

cord

uterus wall

cervix

vagina

It's a fact!

The placenta can't act as a barrier to all harmful substances. In the 1960s the drug thalidomide was given to some pregnant women to help them sleep. Some of them gave birth to babies with no arms or legs.

Eating for two

The pregnant mother must eat sensibly. She may be 'eating for two' but that doesn't mean she has to eat twice as much! **Protein** is needed for the baby to grow. It will also need **calcium** for healthy bones and teeth, and **iron** to build up blood cells.

► In your groups, design a poster to show pregnant women that their habits, good and bad, will affect their babies.

It's a fact!

Some germs can get across the placenta to the fetus. If the mother has German measles it can affect the baby's eyes and heart and cause deafness. Twelve-year old girls are given a rubella injection to stop them catching German measles.

1 What important jobs do each of these do:
a) the placenta?
b) the cord?
c) the fluid sac?

2 What advice would you give to Ruth about keeping healthy during pregnancy?

3 Collect some leaflets or articles giving advice on pregnancy.
Make your own leaflets for an ante-natal clinic.

4 How do you think Jim could have helped Ruth during her pregnancy?
Find out by looking at leaflets and by asking some fathers.

Things to do

Birth and after

Think about what it is like to be a new-born baby.
How is life outside different from life inside the mother?

▶ Copy and complete this table:

	Inside the uterus	After the birth
How does the baby get food?		
How does the baby get oxygen?		
What sort of things does the baby react to?		
How is the baby protected?		

Ruth's baby

Ruth had been pregnant for 36 weeks.

One day she felt the muscles in her uterus squeezing (**contracting**).
This was the start of **labour**.

Jim took her to the hospital straight away.
He and the **midwife** helped her to get ready for the birth.
Her contractions were getting stronger and coming more often.
Soon the sac of liquid around the baby broke.

After several hours of gradual pushing by Ruth, the baby was born.
It came out head first through her vagina. It was a girl!

She was still joined to Ruth by the cord. The doctor cut this.
Later the rest of the cord and the placenta came out.
This is called the **afterbirth**.

Ruth rested and the baby slept. Soon the baby was hungry.
She had milk from her mother's breasts.
Ruth and Jim decided to call her Laura.

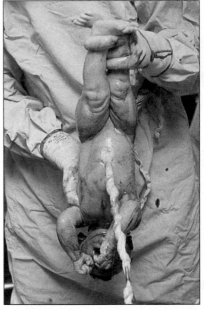

This baby has just been born. The cord is about to be tied and cut.

▶ Write down your answers to the following questions.
a How did the baby come out of Ruth's body?
b What was the cord for?
c Where was your cord joined to your body at birth?
d What is the afterbirth?

Looking after baby

Humans take care of their babies.

▶ When you were a baby you needed things to make you feel happy and safe. You also needed things in order to grow and keep healthy.

Make a list of the things you needed.

Babies have:
- **physical** needs, like warmth, and
- **emotional** needs, like being loved.

▶ Look at the pictures and see if you can find some of these needs.
Copy and complete this table:

Physical needs	Emotional needs
warmth	being loved

▶ Discuss in groups what you think the following need from their parents:
- a baby
- a 6-year-old
- you.

Left holding the baby

▶ You have been asked to baby sit. Some friends want you to look after Ben, their 18-month-old baby boy for an afternoon.

Write down what you think his physical and emotional needs are.

How can you meet these needs?

---

1 Copy and complete:
The baby is ready to be born after .... weeks. Normally it is lying .... downwards inside the .... of the mother. It .... out through the mother's .... It moves because of .... of the wall of the uterus.

2 How do you think Jim could have helped Ruth during the birth of their baby?

3 Mothers take their babies to the clinic for check-ups (post-natal care). What sort of things do you think the nurse would check?

4 Look at the table below.
a) Draw a bar chart to show the time between fertilisation and birth in the animals listed.
b) Can you see any pattern?

Animal	Time between fertilisation and birth (months)
hamster	0.5
rabbit	1
cat	2
sheep	5
chimpanzee	7
human	9
horse	11
elephant	20

Things to do

Adolescence

Adolescence is a time of change in our lives. During this time each of us changes from a child into a young adult. Our bodies change and so do our emotions.

▶ Have you found a photograph of you when you were 8 or 9 years old? Swap your photograph with that of your friend.

How do you think your friend has changed?

How do you think you've changed?

Puberty is the first stage of adolescence. Most changes in our bodies occur at this time. Not everybody starts puberty at the same time. Girls usually start before boys.

▶ Look at some of the pupils in Years 8 and 9 of your school. Can you see that many of the girls are taller than many of the boys?

If you look at those in Year 11 what do you see? Many of the boys will have caught up with and overtaken the girls.

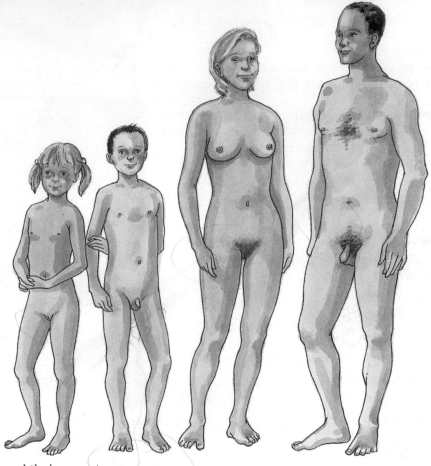

▶ Look at this picture of 9-year-old children and their parents.

a Write down the changes that have taken place between the boy and the man.

b Write down the changes that have taken place between the girl and the woman.

There are some other changes that occur that you can't see in the picture. The table opposite lists some of these changes:

What do you think causes all of these changes?

In a word the answer is '**hormones**'. Hormones are chemicals made in our bodies. Female sex hormones are made by the ovaries. Male sex hormones are made by the testes.

Girls	Boys
ovaries start to release eggs	testes start to make sperms
monthly periods begin	voice becomes deeper ('breaks')

It's a fact!

Many teenagers get spots or acne. This is not due to dirtiness. It's caused by sex hormones and disappears once adolescence is over.

66

Periods

One change that happens to girls during puberty is they start having periods. So what do we mean by a period?

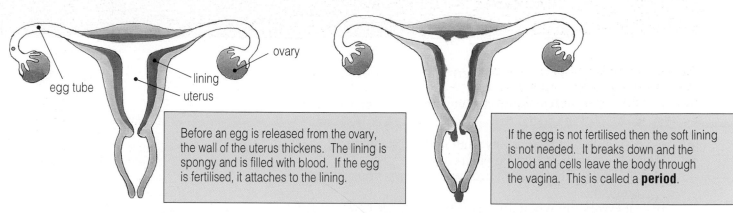

egg tube
lining
uterus
ovary

Before an egg is released from the ovary, the wall of the uterus thickens. The lining is spongy and is filled with blood. If the egg is fertilised, it attaches to the lining.

If the egg is not fertilised then the soft lining is not needed. It breaks down and the blood and cells leave the body through the vagina. This is called a **period**.

A girl's period lasts about 3 to 7 days. Periods usually occur once every 28–31 days, but this can vary. At first periods may be irregular, but as a girl gets older her periods become more regular. Girls can choose sanitary towels or tampons to absorb the flow of blood.

c What do you think would happen to the lining of the uterus if the egg was fertilised?

Emotions

During adolescence our feelings also start to change.
Suddenly we find the opposite sex more interesting and attractive.
Girls and boys start to look at themselves and ask questions such as:
Am I normal?
Am I too tall or too fat?
Am I attractive to the opposite sex?

▶ In groups, discuss some 'problem letters' written by teenagers.

Do you think the writers are right to be worried?

Write a reply to one of them.

---

1 Copy this diagram and use it to answer the following questions.

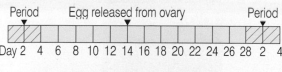

Period ▼   Egg released from ovary ▼   Period ▼
Day 2 4 6 8 10 12 14 16 18 20 22 24 26 28 2 4

a) How often does a period occur?
b) How long does a period last?
c) On which day is an egg released?
d) Mark on your diagram the time when fertilisation is most likely to occur.

2 Why do you think the thick lining of the uterus is needed?

3 An egg is released from a girl's ovary on April 2nd. When will the next egg probably be released:
● April 30th
● May 8th or
● April 14th?

4 Why won't a woman have a period when she is pregnant?

Things to do

Questions

1 a) What happens to human sperms after they are released into the woman's body?
     b) What happens to a human egg after it has been fertilised?

2 Do you think that there is any truth in these statements? Write down your reasons in each case.
     a) "I've heard that the first time you have sex you can't get pregnant."
     b) "If I work out when my egg is released, it is perfectly safe to have sex at other times."

3 Look at this diagram of twin babies inside the uterus:
     a) Write down the letters A to D and give the name of each part.
     b) What do you think happens to each of these parts during birth?
     c) The twin on the right side of the diagram is better placed for birth than the twin on the left. In what way?

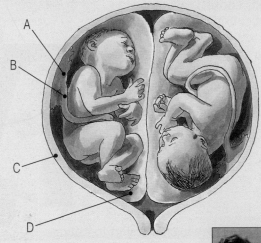

4 How do you think a father can be helpful:
     a) during the mother's pregnancy?
     b) during the birth?

5 a) Make a list of 4 ways in which a girl's body changes during puberty.
     b) Make a list of 4 ways in which a boy's body changes during puberty.

6 Karen is 14. She says:
     "I seem to fall out with my parents all the time these days. We argue about where I go, the friends I'm with, even the clothes I wear! We used to get on so well together. Is it my fault? What's happening to me?"
     What advice can you give Karen?

7 Mark and Sharon are both 16. They have been going steady for two years. Its Friday night and Sharon has had to go away for the weekend with her parents to a wedding. Mark has nothing to do. His mates call round for him and persuade him to go to the local club disco.
     At the disco, Mark notices Joanne. His mates say Joanne has always fancied him …

     Write 2 different endings to the story. In one, show that Mark has a caring, responsible attitude towards Sharon. In the other, show that he hasn't.

Magnetism and Electricity

6

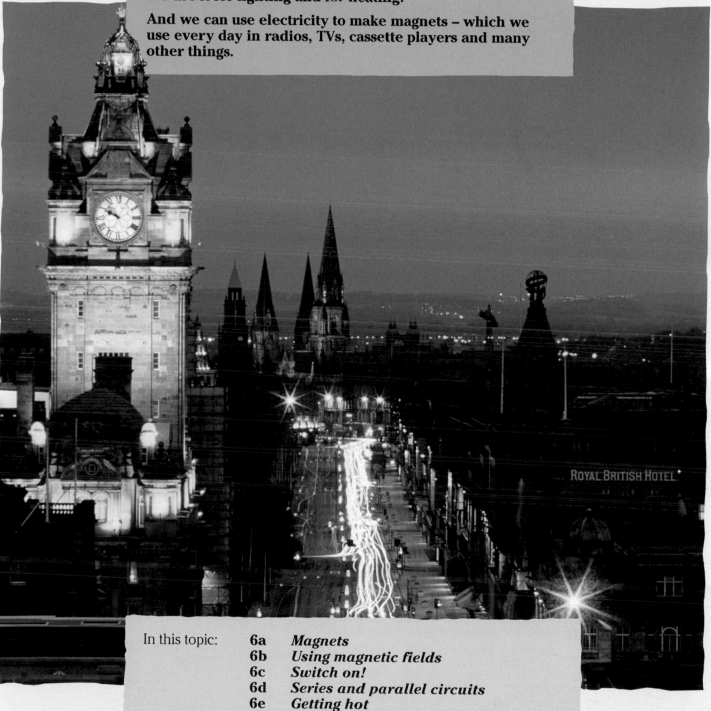

Electricity is important to all of us.
Our lives would be very different without it.

We use it for lighting and for heating.

And we can use electricity to make magnets – which we use every day in radios, TVs, cassette players and many other things.

ROYAL BRITISH HOTEL

Magnets

a   If you spill some pins on the floor, what is the best way to pick them up?

If you use a magnet, the pins stick to the ends or **poles** of the magnet.

b   Can you use a magnet to pick up paper off the floor? Why not?

Sailors used to hang a magnet from a piece of string, so that it could swing freely:

c   Why did the sailors do this?

d   What is the name of this instrument?

a compass

The end of the magnet that points to the North is called the North-pole (N-pole) of the magnet.

e   What is the name given to the other end of the magnet?

Some things are magnetic, and some are not.

f   Which of these are magnetic: wood, iron, plastic, paper, steel, rubber, copper, brass?

Making a magnet

A piece of iron or steel can be magnetised by stroking it several times with a magnet:

g   Why is it sometimes useful to have a screwdriver which is magnetic?

If a magnet is heated until it is red-hot, it becomes **demagnetised**.

Magnetic fields

Magnets can **attract** (pull) or **repel** (push) other magnets.
A **N**-pole repels another **N**-pole.
A **S**-pole attracts a **N**-pole.

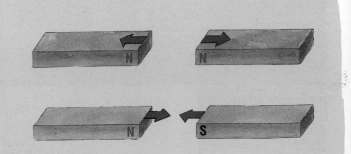

They can do this without touching. This is because a magnet has a **magnetic field** round it. Iron and steel are affected by a magnetic field.

The Earth has a magnetic field round it. This field makes a compass point to the North.

h   What happens if a **S**-pole is brought near to a **S**-pole?

Investigating magnetic games

Here are 4 magnetic games. Plan your time carefully to do as many as possible.
For each one, draw a sketch and write down a **scientific** description of what happens.

Race track

Draw a race track and then 'drive' a paper-clip round it.

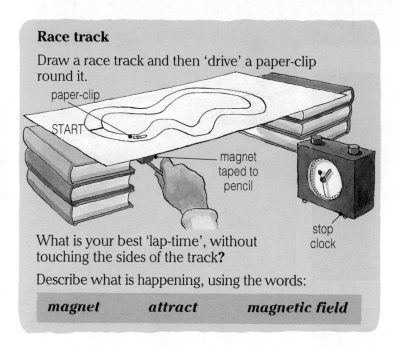

What is your best 'lap-time', without touching the sides of the track?

Describe what is happening, using the words:

magnet	*attract*	*magnetic field*

Coin sorter

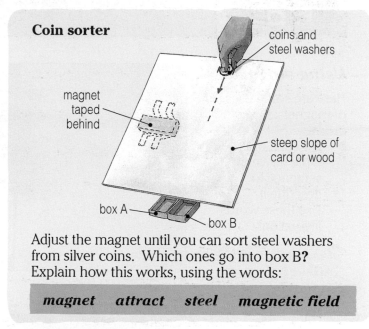

Adjust the magnet until you can sort steel washers from silver coins. Which ones go into box B?
Explain how this works, using the words:

magnet	*attract*	*steel*	*magnetic field*

Identikit face

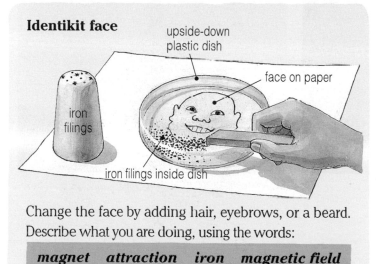

Change the face by adding hair, eyebrows, or a beard.
Describe what you are doing, using the words:

magnet	*attraction*	*iron*	*magnetic field*

Magnetic dogs

Make two 'dogs' like this:

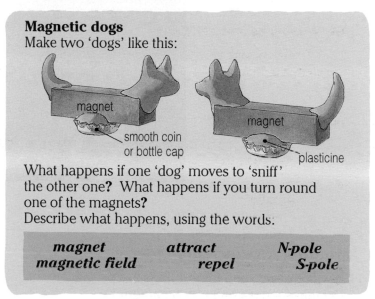

What happens if one 'dog' moves to 'sniff' the other one? What happens if you turn round one of the magnets?
Describe what happens, using the words:

magnet	*attract*	*N-pole*
magnetic field	*repel*	*S-pole*

Things to do

1 Copy and complete:
a) A magnet has a . . . . field round it.
b) The . . . . field is strongest near the ends of the magnet, called the North-. . . . and the South-. . . .
c) A piece of iron can be magnetised by . . . . it with a . . . . It can be demagnetised by . . . . it.
d) The Earth has a magnetic . . . . round it.
e) A N-pole . . . . another N-pole.
A S-pole . . . . a N-pole.

2 Suppose you are given a bowl of sugar with some iron filings mixed up in it.
a) How could you separate the sugar from the iron filings?
b) Can you think of a completely different way of doing this?

3 Design an investigation to compare the strengths of two bar-magnets.
What equipment would you need? Draw a diagram.
How would you make it a fair test?

Using magnetic fields

Using magnets

Here are some uses of magnets:

▶ For each one, write down a sentence to describe it. Use these words if you can:

**magnet   pole
attract   repel
magnetic field**

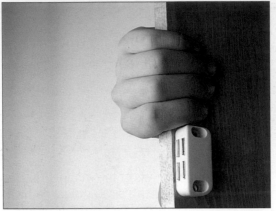

a Cupboard door catch

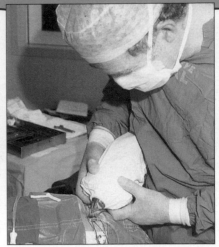

c In an eye hospital

b A compass

d Magnetic crane in a scrap-yard

Making an electromagnet

The door-catch and the compass use permanent magnets.
But the crane uses an **electromagnet**.
An electromagnet can be switched on and off.

▶ Use the diagram to make your own electromagnet:

Warning: only connect the battery for a few seconds or it will soon go flat!

● How can you test the strength of your electromagnet? Try it.

● What happens when you switch off the current?

● Can you think how you could make it a stronger magnet? If you have time, try it.

Electromagnets are used in all electric motors, door-bells, loudspeakers and TV sets.

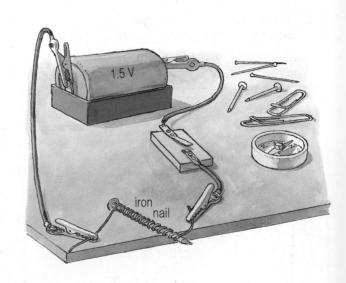

1.5 V

iron
nail

Magnetic fields

We cannot see the magnetic field round a magnet, but we can find out the shape of it.

Put a magnet under a sheet of paper as shown:

Sprinkle some iron filings over the paper and then tap the paper.

Look carefully at the pattern that appears. Can you see that it is the same shape as in the diagram?

Make a sketch of the shape you get.

The iron filings act as tiny compasses, and point along the magnetic field.
The curved lines are called **field lines** or **lines of flux**.

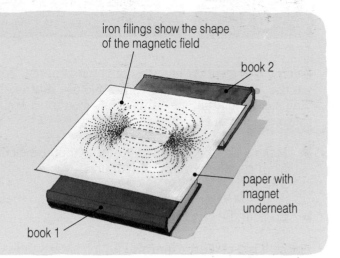
iron filings show the shape of the magnetic field
book 2
paper with magnet underneath
book 1

Here is a better way. Use a *plotting compass* to make a map of the magnetic field.

Follow these instructions carefully.

1 Place your magnet on a large sheet of paper and draw round it to mark its position.

2 Choose a starting point near the N-pole of the magnet and mark it with a pencil dot.

3 Put the 'tail' of the compass pointer over your dot, and then draw a second dot at the 'head' of the compass pointer.

4 Move the compass along until its tail is over the dot, and continue in the same way.

5 Dot the path of the compass as it leads you through the magnetic field. Join up the dots to make a smooth line.

6 Choose another starting point, to get different field lines, as in the diagram.

● Is it the same shape as before?

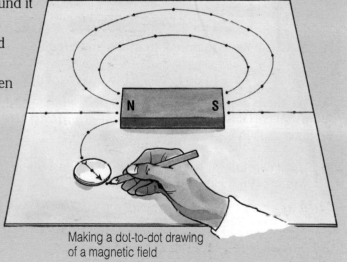
Making a dot-to-dot drawing of a magnetic field

---

1 Make a survey of all the things in your house that use electromagnets.
(Hint: see the bottom of the opposite page.)

2 Imagine you are a vet, and a dog is brought to you with a steel splinter in its eye. Describe how you might help it.

3 Design a game which uses an electromagnet.

4 Suppose you wake up tomorrow morning and find that no electromagnets work any more. Write about how your life would be changed.
(Hint: see the bottom of the opposite page.)

5 Plan an investigation to see if iron can be made into a magnet more easily than steel. How would you make it a fair test?

Things to do

Switch on!

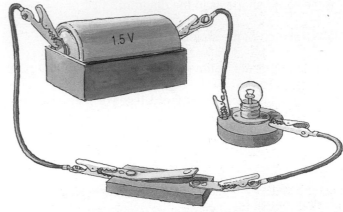

Electricity is a very useful way of getting energy. Sometimes we use a **battery** and sometimes we use **mains** electricity. Mains electricity can be dangerous – you must not use it in these experiments.

▶ Make a list of things in your home that use electricity from a battery or from the mains.

▶ Look at the **circuit** shown here.

Below it is a **circuit diagram**, which shows the same circuit, in symbols.

Find the symbol for: a) the **battery** (or '**cell**')
b) the **lamp bulb**
c) the **switch**.

▶ Copy this circuit diagram and label the symbols.

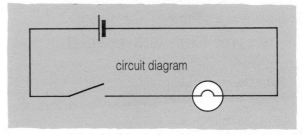

circuit diagram

▶ Now use the equipment to make this circuit.

What do you have to do to make the bulb light up**?**

We say there is an electric **current** flowing in the circuit. A current can flow *only if there is a complete circuit* with no gaps in it.

▶ Look carefully at a switch. What happens when you press it**?** How does it work**?**

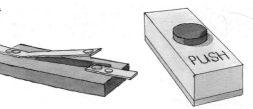

Conductors and insulators

A material that will let an electric current flow through it is called a **conductor**.
An **insulator** will not let electricity go through it.

You can use the circuit shown in the diagram to test some materials, to see if they are conductors or insulators.

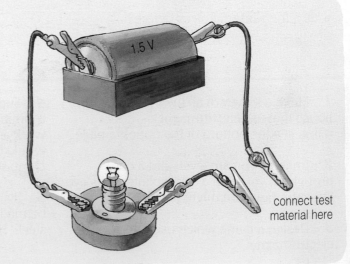

connect test material here

● Draw a circuit diagram of this circuit.

● Say what would happen when these materials are tested:
a an iron nail **b** copper wire **c** a wooden match
d a brass key **e** a 10p coin **f** a plastic spoon
g rubber band **h** paper-clip **i** pencil **j** paper.

● Is air a conductor or an insulator? How do you know?

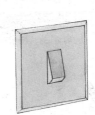

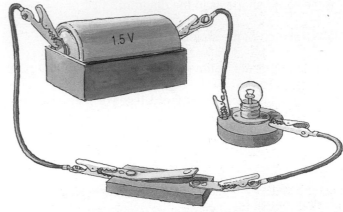

Electric games

Choose **one** of these games and draw a detailed diagram of how you would make it. Show your plan to your teacher, and then make your game.

Steady hand game

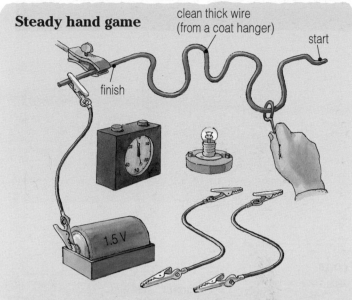

clean thick wire (from a coat hanger)

start

finish

1.5 V

Is your hand steady enough for you to be a surgeon or a vet?

- How many seconds does it take you?
- Can you do it with your other hand?
- Can you count backwards from 99 at the same time?

Quiz game

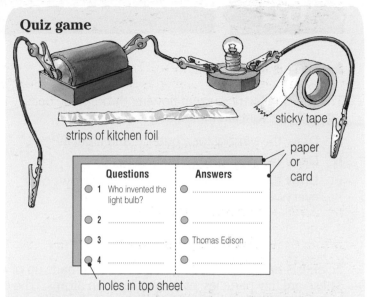

sticky tape

strips of kitchen foil

paper or card

Questions	Answers
1 Who invented the light bulb?	....
2	....
3	Thomas Edison
4	....

holes in top sheet

- How can you use the kitchen foil to connect a 'Question' hole to the correct 'Answer' hole (but so it can't be seen)?
- What can you use to insulate the strips of foil from each other?
- Make up your own science questions (and answers) to test your friends.

► Write down how your game works, using the words:

battery **connecting wire** **complete circuit** **electric current** **conductor** **insulator**

---

1 Copy and complete:
a) Mains electricity can be very . . . .
b) When a bulb lights up it shows that an electric . . . . is flowing.
c) For an electric current to flow, there must be a . . . . circuit, with no gaps in it.

2 Answering carefully,
a) Explain what you mean by:
   i) a conductor   ii) an insulator.
b) Draw and label the circuit symbols for
   i) a battery   ii) a bulb   iii) a switch.
c) Explain what happens when you operate a switch.

3 Suppose you wake up tomorrow morning and find there is no electricity at all in the world. How would your life be different?

4 Mr. Smith is deaf and can't hear his door-bell.
a) Draw a circuit diagram to show how you would connect a bulb to light up when a visitor presses the switch.
b) How would you change it to light another bulb in his kitchen as well as one in his living-room? Draw a circuit diagram.

5 Design a poster to warn young children not to poke at mains sockets or electric fires.

6 Design an investigation to find out if salty water (brine) is a conductor or an insulator.

7 Find out what you can about the life of Michael Faraday.

Things to do

Series and parallel circuits

▶ Look at this diagram:

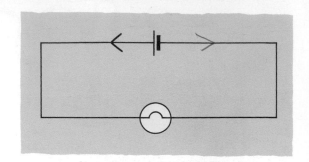

There is an electric current flowing through the battery and through the wires in the bulb.

a Draw the symbol for a battery, and label it.

b Draw the symbol for a bulb (a lamp).

c Draw this circuit diagram, and mark arrows on it everywhere you think there is a current.

Scientists have discovered that electricity is made up of **electrons**. These are tiny particles, even smaller than atoms. The electrons travel through the wires.

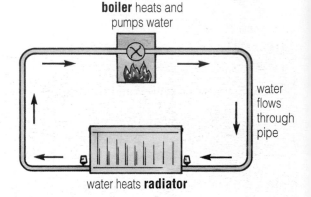

boiler heats and pumps water

water flows through pipe

water heats **radiator**

An electric current is rather like water flowing through a pipe. Look at this diagram of the central-heating pipes in a house:

d Which part of the diagram do you think is like a **battery**? (Hint: a battery pushes electrons round a circuit.)

e Which part of the diagram do you think is most like a **bulb**? (Hint: a bulb is heated up by the electrons going through it.)

Series circuit

The water goes through the boiler, and then the same water goes through the radiator.
We say they are **in series**.

In the same way, the electrons go through the battery and then they go through the bulb, and then back to the battery.
It is a **series circuit**.

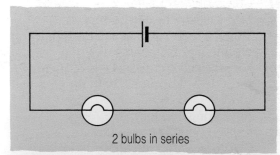

2 bulbs in series

▶ Connect up this series circuit:

f Do both bulbs light up? Is a current going through both bulbs?

g Now unscrew **one** of the bulbs. What happens? Why does this happen?

h Christmas tree lights are often connected in series. What happens then if **one** of the bulbs breaks?

i How do you know that the lights in your house are not wired in series?

Parallel circuits

Look at this circuit, and its circuit diagram below:

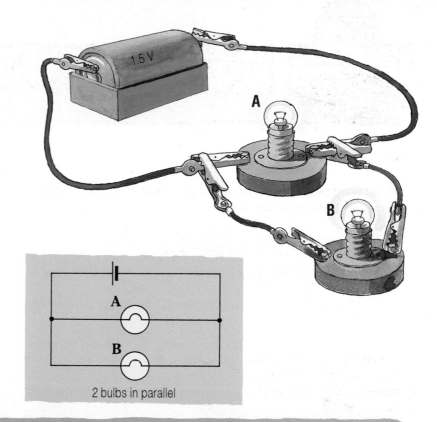

This is a **parallel circuit**.
There are two paths for the current to flow along, with a bulb in each path.
We say the two paths are **in parallel**.

When the electrons travel from the battery, **some** of them go through bulb **A** and **the rest** of them go through bulb **B**.

▶ Connect up this parallel circuit:

j Do both bulbs light up? Is a current going round both paths?

k Now unscrew **one** of the bulbs. Why does the other bulb stay on?

l Are the lights in your house connected in series or in parallel? How do you know?

2 bulbs in parallel

Analysing circuits

Here is a circuit diagram for 2 lights in a doll's house:

Use your finger to follow the path of the electrons from the battery through the bulb **P** and back to the battery. **If your finger has to go through a switch, then this switch is needed to put on the light**.

m Which switch is needed to switch on bulb **P**?

n Which switch is needed for bulb **Q**?

Use the same method to find out the answers to these questions:

o How would you switch on bulb **X**?

p How would you switch on bulb **Y**?

q Are the bulbs **X** and **Y** connected in series or in parallel?

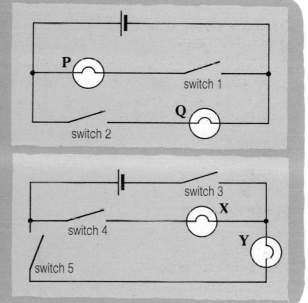

---

1 Copy and complete:
a) In an electric circuit, tiny . . . . move through the wires.
b) If the same current goes through two bulbs, then the bulbs are in . . . .
c) If the current splits up to go through two different paths, we say the paths are in . . . .

2 Design a burglar alarm so that if a burglar steps on your door-mat, an electric bell rings.

3 A torch contains a battery, a switch and a bulb in series.
a) Draw a circuit diagram of this.
Suppose your torch is broken.
b) Describe, with a diagram, how you could test the bulb.
c) How could you test the battery?

4 Jim needs a circuit for his caravan, so that 3 bulbs, each with its own switch, can work from a car battery. Draw a circuit diagram for Jim.

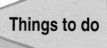

Things to do

Getting hot

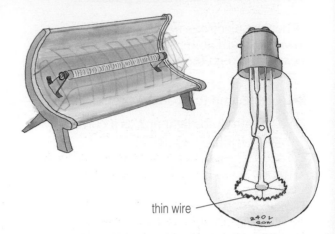

We often use electricity to heat things.

▶ Make a list of all the things in your house that use electricity to get hot.

The thin wire inside a light bulb glows white-hot.
This is because the thin wire has a **resistance** to the current.
As the electrons are forced through this thin wire, they heat it up.

An insulator has a very high resistance, and so the current cannot flow. The electrons cannot get through.

A copper wire has a very low resistance. It is a good conductor.
The electrons can get through easily.

thin wire

Investigating resistance

Connect up this circuit:

- What happens when the crocodile clips are close together? What happens if you move them apart?

- Write a short report saying what you did and what you found.

Your circuit has a *variable resistance*.
You can vary the amount of resistance it has.

Now look carefully at a **variable resistor**:
How does it work?

Connect the variable resistor to your battery and bulb.

What happens when you move the slider? Why?

Draw a circuit diagram of this circuit.

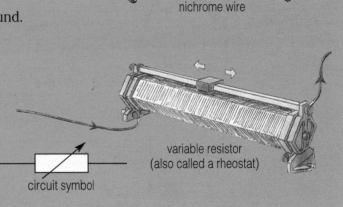

nichrome wire

variable resistor
(also called a rheostat)

circuit symbol

Now look at an **ammeter**.
An ammeter measures the size of a current. It measures it in **amperes** (also called **amps** or **A**).

Connect your battery, bulb, variable resistor and an ammeter in series. *Take care* to connect the red (+) terminal on the ammeter to the + (the button) on the battery.

What happens as you vary the resistance?

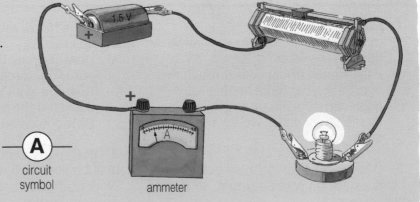

circuit
symbol

ammeter

Fuses for safety

▶ Connect up this circuit:

Put on safety spectacles. Then look carefully at the thin wire while you press the switch. What happens?

▶ Write down what you think is happening, using the words:

> **battery   complete circuit**
> **current   amperes   heating**

The thin wire has melted or **fused**.
When it fuses, it stops the current flowing.
It is a safety device. We call it a **fuse**.

A fuse is a weak part of the circuit. It breaks if there is a fault which lets too much current flow.

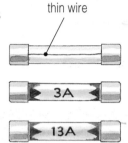

Every mains plug has a fuse inside it.
You can buy fuses with different ratings, such as 3 amp or 13 amp.
A table lamp or TV needs a 3 A fuse.
An electric fire needs a 13 A fuse.

Using the wrong fuse in a TV?

Mains plug

▶ Look carefully at the diagram of a mains plug:
It is very **very** important that the coloured wires are connected to the correct places.

Why is the cord grip important?

▶ Draw a safety poster to help you remember the correct way to wire a plug.

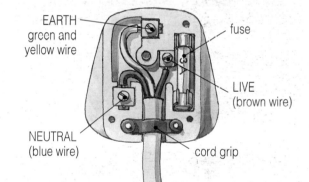

---

1 Copy and complete:
a) A good conductor has a .... resistance.
An insulator has a .... resistance.
b) The current in a circuit can be varied using a .... resistor (also called a ....).
c) An ammeter measures the .... in a circuit, in .... or A.
d) A fuse .... if the current is too big.
e) In a mains plug the brown wire is called the .... wire and must go to the fuse.
The green/yellow wire is the .... wire and must go to the .... pin.
The blue wire is the .... wire.

2 Where might you use a variable resistor (rheostat) in a theatre? Draw a circuit diagram suitable for a toy theatre.

3 Draw a circuit diagram of the ammeter circuit that you used. Label the symbols.

4 What can you say about the thickness of the wire in a 3 A fuse compared with a 13 A fuse?
Which one has the bigger resistance?

5 What might happen if you put a 13 A fuse in a plug for a TV, and the TV was faulty?

6 Draw a circuit with a battery, 2 bulbs in parallel, each controlled by a switch, and an ammeter measuring the total current taken by the bulbs.
Where would you put a variable resistor to dim one of the bulbs?

Things to do

Questions

1 Design a 'magnetic fishing game' for young children.
You could use a magnet, paper-clips, card, string and a stick.
Draw a diagram and make a set of rules for the game.

2 Design a poster to warn children against climbing electric pylons or going on to electric railway lines.

3 Draw a labelled diagram of a light bulb.
Which parts are: a) insulators?   b) conductors?

4 In the circuit shown in the diagram, what happens if:
a)   switch **A** only is closed?
b)   switch **B** only is closed?
c)   **A** and **B** are closed?
d)   Are the bulbs in series or in parallel?

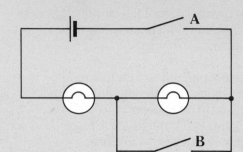

5 a)   An electric saw needs 2 switches for safety.
Design a circuit so that both switches must be 'on' to start the saw, but only one switch need be turned 'off' to stop the saw.
b)   A bank needs an alarm system.
Design a circuit that has a battery and an alarm bell that can be switched on by 2 separate push-buttons
c)   Which of these two circuits (a or b) could you use for door-bell switches at your front door and back door?

6 This diagram shows one kind of ammeter.
What are the readings **a**, **b**, **c**, **d**?

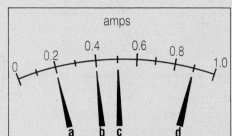

7 Draw a circuit diagram to show how two 6 volt bulbs can be lit brightly from two 3 volt batteries.

8 Each of the pictures below shows an unsafe situation.
For each one:
i)   write a sentence about what is wrong, and
ii)   say what should be done to make it safe.

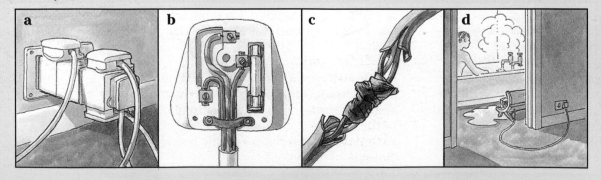

Matter

7

The Eiffel Tower in Paris is about 300 metres high.
But did you know its height can change?
In summer it is taller than in winter.
The difference can be 10 cm.
Finding out about matter might help to explain why ...

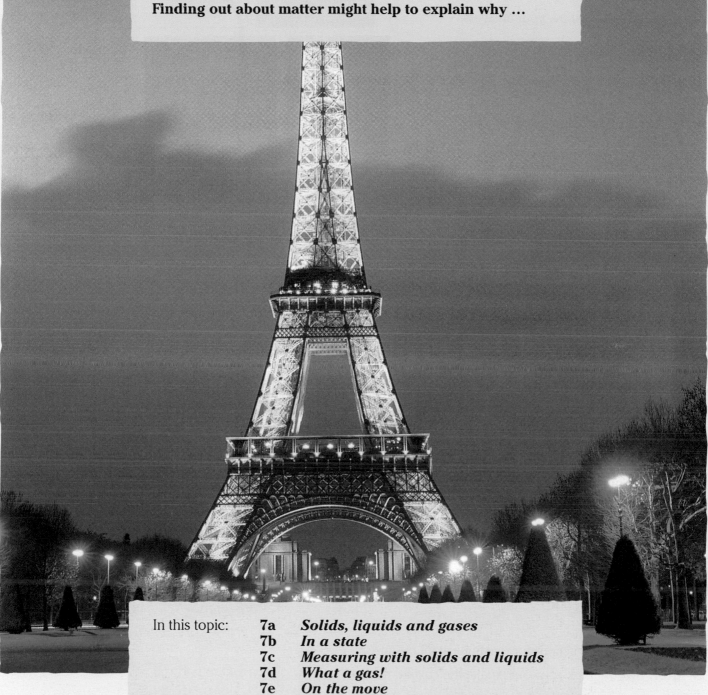

Solids, liquids and gases

7a

▶ Look at these photographs of substances you might find at home.

Which are solids? Which are liquids? Which are gases?

Make a table to show your answers.

You might be able to tell easily which things are solids, which are liquids and which are gases. It can be hard to explain *how* you can tell!

▶ Observe the samples your teacher will give you.
In your group write down some differences between the way solids, liquids and gases behave.

Make a table to show your answers. These are the **properties** of solids, liquids and gases.

Some substances are difficult to classify.

Think about custard!

You can have liquid custard.
It's easy to pour.
It can be stirred.
It takes the shape of its container.

When custard sets it behaves like a solid.
It cannot be poured.
It cannot be stirred.
It has its own shape.

Is custard solid or liquid?

▶ Look at the instructions for making instant custard:

a How do you think you could make the custard thicker?

b How could you make the custard more runny?

c How could you make sure the custard is smooth?

Empty one sachet into a measuring jug.
Add BOILING WATER to $\frac{3}{4}$ pint (425 ml) mark.

Looking at solids, liquids and gases

Squashing

- Put the top tightly on a plastic bottle filled with air.
  Squeeze the bottle with your hands.
  Can you squash the bottle inwards?

- Now fill the plastic bottle with water.
  Put the top on tightly again.
  Try to squeeze the bottle.

- Take a piece of rock. Squeeze it with your hands.

d What do you notice? Try to explain your results.

e What do they tell you about solids, liquids and gases?

Watching

- Drop a crystal in a beaker of water.
  Leave it for a while. Watch.

f What do you notice? Try to explain your results.

g What do they tell you about solids and liquids?

Smelling

- Take the top off the bottle your teacher will give you.
  Hold it 10 cm away from you.

h What do you notice? Try to explain your results.

i What do they tell you about gases?

 Look at your table about how solids, liquids and gases behave.
Can you add some more ideas to the table now?

---

1 Fill in the blanks with either 'liquids' or 'solids'.
.... are runny.
.... are hard.
.... can be poured.
.... take the shape of the container.
.... cannot be stirred.
.... have a fixed shape.
.... and .... cannot be easily squashed.

2 Some substances are difficult to classify as liquids or solids. Custard is one example. Write down 3 other examples.

3 Write a paragraph about liquids.
Include the following words:

wet	pour	thick	thin	drip
	flow	container	freeze	

4 Write a paragraph about gases.
Include the following words:

squash	air	smell	light
	fizzy	balloon	

Things to do

In a state

7b

You can describe substances as **solids**, **liquids** and **gases**.
These are the 3 **states of matter**.

Which is
. . .the solid?
. . .the liquid?
. . .the gas?

Particles

You have already seen that solids, liquids and gases behave in different ways.

We can explain the differences using a theory.
Scientists believe that everything is made of tiny **particles**.

In solids, liquids and gases the particles are arranged in different ways.

The 3 drawings opposite represent the 3 ways:

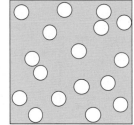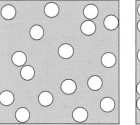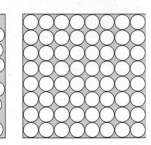

▶ In your group discuss which drawing represents:
- a solid
- a liquid
- a gas.

Your table of solid, liquid and gas properties should help you to decide.

Check your ideas with your teacher.

▶ Copy the particle arrangements shown above.
Label each one as either solid, liquid or gas.

Do you think particles move   … in solids?
                                … in liquids?
                                … in gases?

Give reasons for your ideas.

Warming a solid

What happens to the length of a wire when it is heated?

Predict what will happen in the experiment shown opposite.

Now try it out.

⚠ Care – hot wires can burn.

Warm the wire with a Bunsen burner.

What happens to the length of the wire?

Use the idea of *particles* to explain what you see.

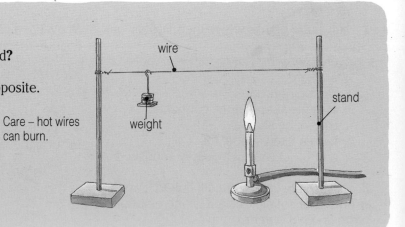

84

Warming a liquid

Fill a test-tube with water.
Put a rubber stopper and glass tube in it, as shown in the diagram opposite.
Mark the water level above the stopper.

Predict what will happen when the tube is put in a beaker of hot water.

Now try it out.

What happens to the volume of a liquid when it is warmed?

What happens when the liquid is cooled again?

Use the idea of *particles* to explain what you see.

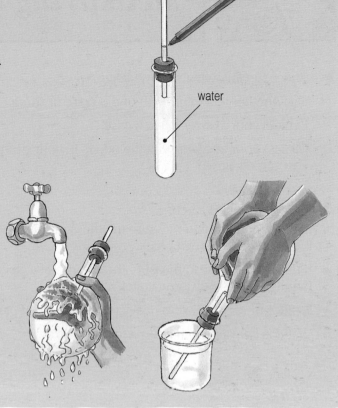
water

Warming a gas

Predict what you think will happen in this experiment.

Take a flask fitted with a stopper and a glass tube.
Run cold water on to the outside for 3 minutes.
Put the glass tube into a beaker of water.
Warm the outside of the flask with your hands.

Now try the experiment.

Use the idea of *particles* to explain what you see.

When things get bigger, we say they **expand**.
When things get smaller, we say they **contract**.

Gases, liquids and solids **expand** when heated.

a Which expands most, a gas, a liquid or a solid?

---

1 Copy and complete using some of the words in the box:

melting	lumps	large	small
solids	gases	liquids	particles
same	contract	hot	expand

a) The three states of matter are . . . . , ... and . . . .
b) . . . . and . . . . are harder to compress (squeeze together) than . . . .
c) Everything is made of . . . .
d) The particles are very . . . .
e) Oven shelves fit more tightly in . . . . ovens.
f) Gases, liquids and solids . . . . when warmed.

2 Which of the following is the best substance to use to fill bicycle tyres? Why?

water	compressed air	wood

3 The label on a lemonade bottle shows the contents:

> water, citric acid, flavourings, carbon dioxide, artificial sweetener

a) Name one substance in the list that is:
   i) a liquid   ii) a gas.
b) There is normally a lot of sugar in fizzy drinks. Which substance in the list replaces sugar?
c) Why do you think that sugar is not used here?
d) Is sugar a solid, liquid or gas?

Things to do

Measuring with solids and liquids

▶ Check the following statements.

Say whether you think each one is *true* or *false*.

Explain your answer in each case.

Discuss your answers with the others in your group. Can you all agree?

- Solids are denser than gases.
- It takes more time to measure the mass of shampoo than the mass of a wooden block.
- It takes more time to measure the volume of a piece of rock than the volume of some water.
- A piece of rock is always heavier than a piece of plastic.
- Water is heavier when it turns to solid ice.

Are solids denser than gases?

Melting

If you heat a solid, you can turn it into a liquid. We say that the solid **melts**.

▶ Make a list of 6 things you have seen melt, e.g. butter, …

The temperature when a solid melts (turns to liquid) is called the **melting point**.

This is the same temperature as when the liquid freezes (turns to solid).

This temperature is also called the **freezing point**.

▶ Look at the melting point values in the table.

a Which substance has the lowest melting point?

b Which substance has the highest melting point?

c In cold weather, which freezes first, water or alcohol?

d Room temperature is about 25 °C. Which of these substances may be liquids at this temperature? Why can't you be sure?

e On being heated from room temperature, which melts first, aluminium or copper?

f What happens if you keep heating a liquid?

g What happens to the particles when a solid melts?

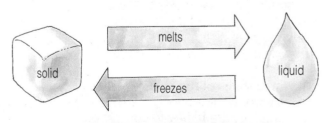

Substance	Melting point in °C
aluminium	660
ice	0
alcohol	−117
iron	1535
copper	1083
mercury	−39
polythene	110

86

Why do we put salt on roads in winter?

To answer this question you could use some temperature sensors.

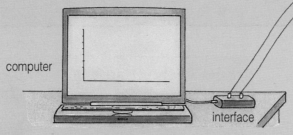

computer

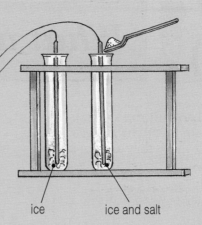

interface

ice   ice and salt

- Place the sensors on the desk carefully.
- Get 2 boiling tubes. Put 10 g of crushed ice into each.
- Add 0.2 g of salt to one tube and stir to mix the ice and salt completely.
- Quickly put one temperature sensor in each tube.
  Make sure it is in the centre of the crushed ice. Wait 1 minute.
- Record the temperature of the ice for 20 minutes.
- Watch the ice carefully.
  Record any changes in its appearance over the 20 minutes.

Draw or print out the graph to show how the temperature changes.
Mark on your graph the point at which the ice melted.

h At the start, what was the **state** of the ice?

i What happened to the solid ice after a while?

j Are the graphs for 'ice on its own' and 'ice and salt' different in any way?

k Describe the shape of the graphs. Which part of the graphs is surprising?

l What effect does salt have on ice?

m Why is salt put on roads in winter?

---

1 Copy and complete each of these statements using one of the words in brackets at the end.
a) Solids are . . . . dense than gases. (less/more)
b) The . . . . when a solid melts is called the melting point. (temperature/time)
c) The . . . . of a liquid is measured in cm³. (mass/volume)
d) When a solid melts it forms . . . . (ice/liquid)
e) When a liquid freezes it turns to . . . . (solid/gas)

2 Cooking oil and alcohol expand when they are heated.
Design an investigation to see which liquid expands more.

3 Explain how you can measure the density of a piece of rock.
(density $= \dfrac{\text{mass}}{\text{volume}}$)
Use diagrams to help you explain.

4 Explain why **liquids** are used in thermometers.

5 Use the information in the melting point table opposite to draw a bar-chart. Organize the substances in melting point order for your bar-chart.

Things to do

87

7d

What a gas!

Gases are all around you.
The air you are breathing is a gas.
Gases fill any space they are put into.
Gases are made when liquids boil.

LIQUID $\xleftarrow[\text{condenses}]{\text{boils}}$ GAS

The temperature when a liquid boils is called
the **boiling point**.

▶ Some gases are listed in the box opposite.
What do you know about them?
Make a patterned note to show your ideas.
You could start like this:

Gases
hydrogen
oxygen
air
nitrogen
carbon dioxide
chlorine
helium
neon
ozone
carbon monoxide
argon

Use books and ROMs to find extra information.

Air is about $\frac{4}{5}$ th nitrogen and $\frac{1}{5}$ th oxygen. There are also small
amounts of other gases such as carbon dioxide and argon.

less dense
Gases are ~~much lighter~~ than solids and liquids.
Different gases have different ~~masses.~~ *densities*
Nitrogen is slightly lighter than oxygen. Helium is a very light gas.
Carbon dioxide is a heavy gas. *less dense*   *low density*
dense.

Where is the air?

▶ You cannot see the gases in the air.
How do you know the air is all around you?

Discuss this in your group.

Use these photographs to help you with your ideas.

Where is the air?

Making oxygen

The most important gas in the air is **oxygen**.
We need it to breathe. It keeps us alive.

In this experiment you can make some oxygen gas.
You can also test to prove it is there!

Your teacher will show you how to
'collect a gas over water'.

- Put 2 spatula measures of the black
  powder into a conical flask.

- Fit a stopper, a thistle funnel and a
  delivery tube into the flask, as shown in
  the diagram.

- Fill some test-tubes with water.
  You will use these to collect the oxygen.

- Set up your apparatus to collect the gas.

- Pour hydrogen peroxide down the thistle
  funnel.
  ***Do not collect the first few bubbles
  of gas. Why not?***

- Collect 2 or 3 tubes of oxygen gas.
  Put a stopper in each tube.
  Put the tubes in a test-tube rack.

- Light a spill.
  Blow it out so that the tip is glowing.

- Put the glowing spill inside the tube.
  What do you see?

- Draw a picture to show how the particles
  are arranged in the oxygen.

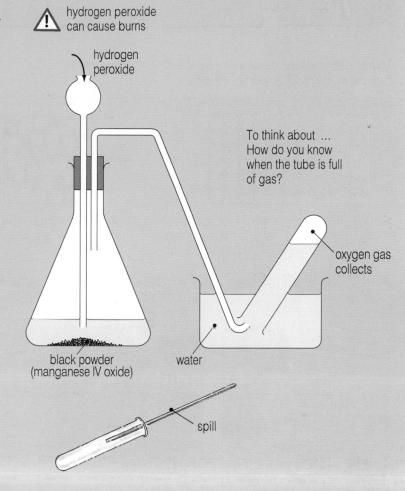

hydrogen peroxide
can cause burns

hydrogen
peroxide

To think about ...
How do you know
when the tube is full
of gas?

oxygen gas
collects

black powder
(manganese IV oxide)

water

spill

Things to do

1 Copy and complete:
a) The air is made up of 2 main gases
   called . . . . and . . . .
b) . . . . is the gas we use to breathe.
c) We breathe out a gas called . . . . dioxide.
d) Helium is a very . . . . gas.
e) We cannot describe the shape of a gas
   because . . . .

2 Laura has drunk all the lemonade in her
bottle. She says the bottle is empty.
Is she right?

3 Which is heavier?

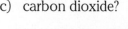

air   oxygen

Explain your idea.

4 Jill has 3 balloons which are filled with
different gases.
Which balloon holds:
a) air?
b) helium?
c) carbon dioxide?

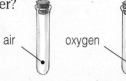

5 Draw a pie-chart to show the
composition of the air.
Label the sections 'oxygen', 'nitrogen' and
'other gases'.

On the move

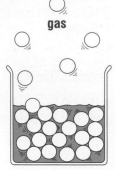

What did you decide about particles? Can they move?
Scientists think that particles move.

gas

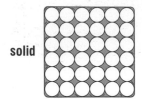

solid

Particles in a solid are close
together. They do not move
about but they do vibrate.

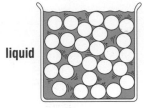

liquid

Particles in a liquid move about.
They are still quite close
together.

Particles in a gas move about quickly.
They move in all directions.
They are further away from each other.

▶ Look at these pictures. They all give clues about gas particles moving.

Phew! I think her perfume is a bit strong.

picture 1

A lovely smell.

picture 2

PETROLEUM SPIRIT
HIGHLY
FLAMMABLE

NO
SMOKING

picture 3

TANKER CRASH LATEST

The tanker was carrying
ammonia. The gas can
affect eyes and breathing.
People living within a
3 mile radius of the crash
were moved from their
homes.

picture 4

The pictures tell you that gas particles can move and mix.
They do this without being stirred or shaken.
This is called **diffusion**.
We say that gases **diffuse**. We could also say "The smell of
perfume is **diffusing** throughout the room".

a Write about 2 lines to say what is happening to the gas particles
in picture 1.

b The roses in picture 2 smell lovely. Draw them and show how
their smell spreads in a room. Use dots to represent particles.
(Hint: lots of dots together mean a strong smell.)

c Why is 'No smoking' important at the petrol station in picture 3?

d Look at picture 4. Why did people living 3 miles from the crash
have to be moved?

e Think of some tests you could carry out to see if liquids or solids
diffuse.
Write down:
• what you would do
• how you would know about any diffusion.

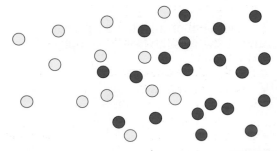

No confusion – it's **diffusion**

Where has it gone?

When some solids are put into a liquid like water, they get smaller.
Some solids disappear.
If the solid disappears, we say it has **dissolved**.

The liquid we get when a solid dissolves is a **solution**.

▶ Think about particles on the move.
Discuss these questions in your group.

- Why does sugar dissolve when you put it into a cup of tea**?**
- Where do the sugar particles go**?**
- Does the sugar dissolve faster in cold tea or hot tea**?**
- Do sugar particles move faster in cold tea or hot tea**?**

Investigating solutions

Jawad was investigating solutions.

He filled a beaker to the 200 cm³ mark with water.

He then used a balance to find the mass of beaker + water.

Mass of beaker + water = __ g

He added sugar granules to the water. He stirred the water until he could not see the sugar. It had dissolved.

He used the balance to find the mass of beaker + sugar solution.

Mass of beaker + sugar solution = __ g

f Predict Jawad's results:
do you think the mass will stay the same**?**
... get smaller**?**
... get bigger**?**

g Why did you choose this answer**?**

Now try Jawad's experiment for yourself.

h What do you find**?**

---

1 Match each of the following descriptions with the correct word.

Description	Word
a) solid disappearing in a liquid	diffusing
b) particles moving and mixing	predicting
c) the liquid made when a solid dissolves	mass
d) saying what you think will happen	solution
e) a measurement made in grams	dissolving

2 Look at the contents of the cupboards in your kitchen.
Do any of the labels or containers talk about dissolving?
Make a note of what is said.

Product	Notes on dissolving
oven cleaner	dissolves grease and baked on food

3 Think about dissolving a sugar cube in water. What could you do to make it dissolve faster?
List your ideas.

Things to do

7f Do you have a solution?

Penny, Mike and Chung were talking about **dissolving** things.

Who do you think was right?

▶ Imagine you are the pupils' teacher.

Try to help this group understand melting and dissolving.

Write down what you would say to each person.

Making a solution

In this experiment you can test some solids to see if they dissolve in water.

- Half fill a test-tube with water.

- Add 1 spatula measure of solid to the water.

- Shake the tube gently for 1 minute.

- Look to see if any of the solid has disappeared. If so, it must have **dissolved**.

- Do the experiment again with other solids.

Solids which dissolve are said to be **soluble**.

Solids which do not dissolve are said to be **insoluble**.

a Which solids are soluble in water?

b Which solids are insoluble in water?

c Penny says "You can use this experiment to see which substance is the most soluble."
Is she right?
Give Penny some advice on how she could improve the experiment.

Sometimes it is hard to tell if a solid has dissolved.

d How could you test to see if any solid has dissolved?

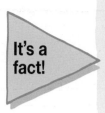
In 1949 a man was charged with murder. He had dissolved his victim's body in concentrated sulphuric acid. He thought he could not be found guilty because there was no body.

... But sulphuric acid does not dissolve everything. The police found the victim's false tooth. The 'acid bath murderer' was found guilty!

Think about dissolving

Hypotheses are ideas about things which always happen.

You can make a hypothesis.
From this you can make a **prediction**.
Then you can collect evidence to see if it is true.

Mike had a hypothesis about dissolving.
He said "I think substances always dissolve faster if they are stirred."
Do you think he was right?

Think about **your own** work on dissolving.
Write down your own hypothesis about dissolving.
Use your ideas about particles to predict what will happen.

Plan an investigation to test your prediction.

How can you make your results reliable?

Ask your teacher if you can carry out your investigation.

1 Copy and complete:
a) Solids which dissolve are called . . . . solids.
b) . . . . solids do not dissolve.
c) A solid is said to dissolve if it . . . . when put in water.

2 Plan an investigation to test Mike's idea about dissolving.

3 Draw particle diagrams to show what you think happens when:
a) a solid melts
b) a solid dissolves in water.

4 Look carefully at the wordsquare. Find as many words as you can about this topic. You should be able to find 11.
Do not mark this book.

D	F	D	Y	M	L	S	C
I	H	I	M	E	O	Z	E
F	G	S	O	L	I	D	X
F	A	S	V	T	E	B	P
U	S	O	E	S	V	B	A
S	O	L	U	T	I	O	N
E	P	V	M	I	X	I	D
J	W	E	D	R	O	L	T

Things to do

93

Questions

1 Imagine you are the teacher of a class of 10-year-olds.
Think about some tests your pupils could do to
classify things as solids or liquids.

Design a worksheet which shows:
- the apparatus pupils need
- clear instructions for each test
- the results expected for solids
- the results expected for liquids.

Make sure your worksheet is interesting!
You could draw diagrams, cartoons or pictures on it.
You could even set some homework!

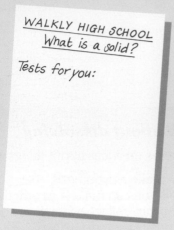

WALKLY HIGH SCHOOL
What is a solid?

Tests for you:

2 Write a paragraph about solids using the following words:

> stir   pour   shape   melt   contract
> freeze   water   ice   expand

3 Choose one of the gases you know about.
Design a poster for 10-year-old children to tell them about
this gas and its uses.

4 Plan an investigation to find out how much gas is given
off by one can of fizzy drink.

5 Explain each of the following statements.
a) Heating a metal top on a glass jar helps
you to remove the top.
b) The Eiffel Tower is smaller in winter
than in summer.
c) Icing on a cake can run.

6 A purple crystal is put into a beaker of water.
It starts to dissolve.
Draw pictures to show what you think will be seen:
a) after 10 minutes   b) after 2 hours   c) after 2 weeks.

7 Design an investigation to show how the temperature of the water
affects the speed at which a solid dissolves in it.

8 What makes a good group discussion?
In this topic you have discussed lots of ideas and problems.
Draw up a set of points to look for, which your teacher could use to
judge how well you discuss.

Sight

Our eyes use light energy, and help us to make sense of the world around us.

In this topic you will learn about light waves and about other types of electromagnetic waves.

8a

See here!

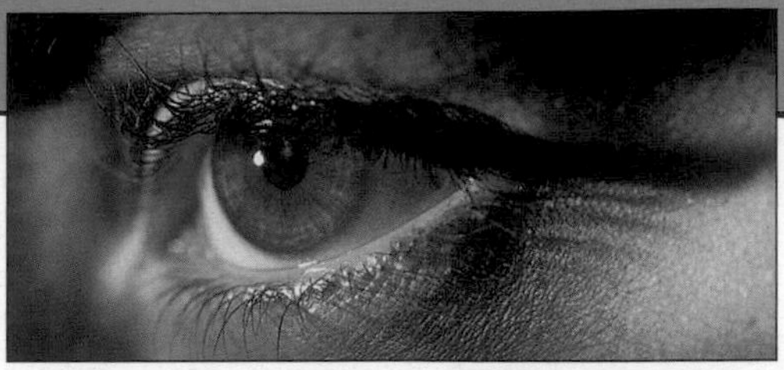

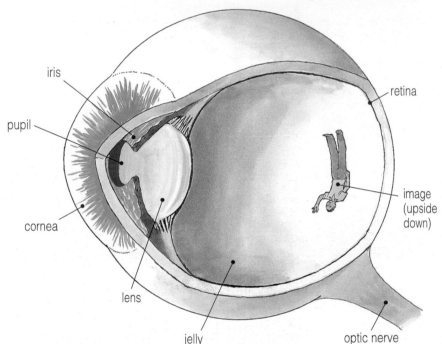

► Close your eyes and think what it would be like to be completely blind.
Write down 3 things that you could not do if you were blind.

► Hold a mirror in front of you, and look at your eye. You are looking at an **image** of your eye.
The coloured part of your eye is called the **iris**.
Make an accurate drawing of your iris.

The dark hole in the middle of your iris is called the **pupil**. This lets the light enter your eye.

► Keep looking in the mirror while you turn your head to point to a dark part of the room and then to a bright window.
Look carefully.
What happens to the size of your pupil?
Why is this?

► Look at this diagram of your eye:
Study the different parts of it.

► Your teacher will give you a copy of this diagram. Fill in the missing words on the sheet.

Diagram labels: iris, pupil, cornea, lens, jelly, retina, image (upside down), optic nerve

How do you see?

Emma has a **hypothesis** about how she can see things:

Tina has a different hypothesis:

• Which hypothesis do you think is correct?

• Write some sentences to explain your reasons.
Try to use these words:

light   reflected   eye   pupil

• Can you think of an investigation that will decide between these two hypotheses?

Emma says: "I think the light always has to travel to my eye and then to the book so that I can see it."

Tina says: "I think the light always has to travel to the book and then be reflected up into my eye."

Are two eyes better than one?

- Do you think you can judge distances better with one eye or two? Write down your prediction.

- Plan a short investigation to test this.
  You can use a quick test of skill such as:
  hold out a pencil in each hand at arm's length and try to make the pencil points touch each other.

- Do your investigation. What do you find?

Most animals have two eyes

Shadows

▶ Shine a torch or a **ray-box** at a white sheet of paper.
  Hold an object so that you see a **shadow** on the screen.

a Why is the screen bright?

b Why is the shadow dark?

c How can you make the shadow larger?

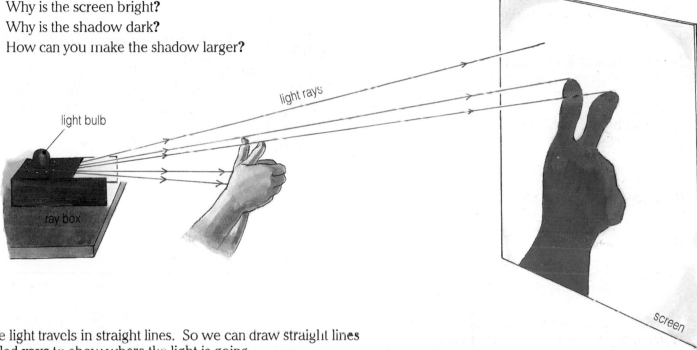

light rays

light bulb

ray box

screen

The light travels in straight lines. So we can draw straight lines
called **rays** to show where the light is going.

d How can you use your ruler to check that the light rays travel in
straight lines?

---

1 Copy and complete:
When I look at this page, the . . . . rays
are reflected off the white paper and then
travel into my . . . . The rays make an
. . . . on my retina. In a dim light my
pupil grows . . . . so that more . . . . can
get into my . . . .

2 In a thunderstorm you see the lightning
and then hear the thunder.
What does this tell you about the speed of
light?

3 Draw a design for a clock that uses
shadows from the Sun.

4 Get a piece of card about 10 cm × 10 cm.
On one side draw a bird (using thick lines).
On the other side draw a cage. Tape a
pencil to the card so that you can spin it
quickly between your hands. What do you
see?
Write a sentence to explain what you think
is happening. Then design a different card.

Things to do

Mirrors and reflections

Light rays can be **reflected**.

You can see this page because light rays are being reflected off the white paper and into your eyes.

Where the light shines on this black ink, it is not reflected – it is **absorbed**.

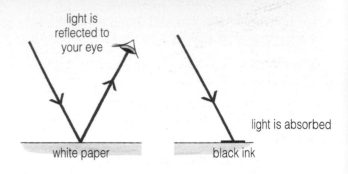

A mirror is a good reflector of light.
When you look in a mirror, you see an **image** of yourself.

▶ Think about all the ways that mirrors are used – in homes, shops and cars. Make a list of all the uses you can think of.

How can you use a mirror on a sunny day to send a message to a distant friend?

If your bedroom is dark, how can you use a mirror to make it look brighter?

A flat mirror is called a **plane** mirror.
Here is an experiment to see what happens when light is reflected off a plane mirror.

The Law of Reflection

Your teacher will give you a Help Sheet with some lines and angles marked on it.

1 Set your plane mirror with its **back** along the line marked 'mirror' (the light is reflected from the silver back of the mirror).

2 Use a ray-box to send a narrow beam of light (a 'ray') along the line marked 20° on the **angle of incidence** scale.

3 Measure the **angle of reflection**. What do you find?

4 Repeat this using different angles of incidence.

5 Write down your conclusion.

• If the angle of incidence was 34°, what do you think the angle of reflection would be? Predict it and then try it.

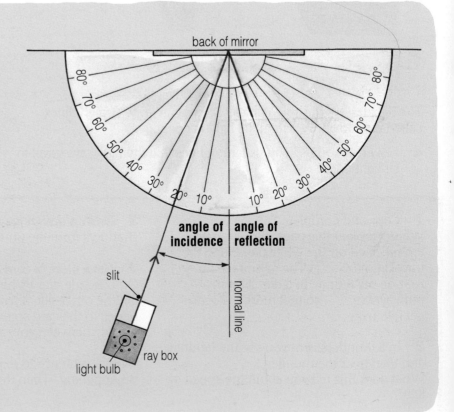

Mirror images

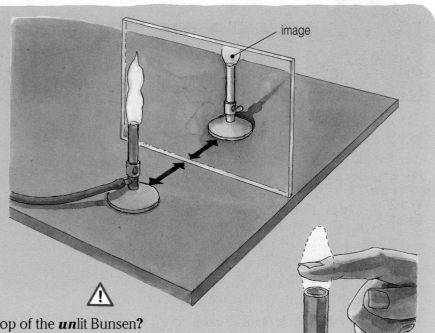

1 Fix a sheet of glass so that it is upright on the table.

2 Put a Bunsen burner with a bright yellow flame in front of it.

3 Look into the 'mirror' to see the image of the flame. Where does it appear to be?

4 Move another **un**lit Bunsen burner until the image of the flame sits exactly on it.

5 Measure the distances of the two Bunsen burners from the glass mirror. What do you find?

6 Try this using different distances.

7 Write down your conclusion.

● What do you see if you put your finger on top of the **un**lit Bunsen?

Curved mirrors

Curved mirrors can be **convex** (like the back of a spoon) or **concave** (like the front of a spoon).

A **concave** mirror is used in a torch and in a car headlight:

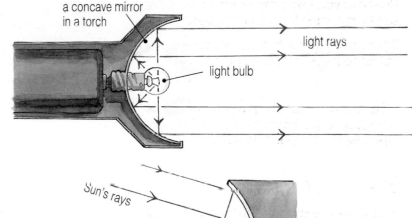

A **concave** mirror is also used in a solar cooker:

This is a cheap source of energy in some countries.

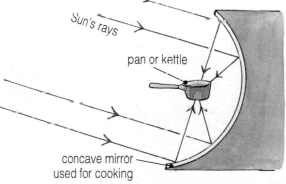

Things to do

1 Look at this notice:

> The Law of Reflection
> The angle of incidence is **equal** to the angle of reflection

a) How can you read it easily?
b) Copy it out correctly.
c) Copy and complete:
The distance from an object to a plane mirror is . . . . to the distance from the . . . . to the mirror.

2 Write your name so that it reads correctly when viewed in a mirror.

3 Where and why might you see:

AMBULANCE

4 Imagine you wake up tomorrow in a world where light is never reflected. Write a story about it.

Bending light

▶ The picture shows a ray of light from the lamp passing through some different materials.

a Explain how the picture shows that light only travels in straight lines.

b Which material lets most light pass through it? This material is **transparent**.

c Which material lets no light pass through it? This material is **opaque**.

d Which material lets only some light pass through it? This material is **translucent**.

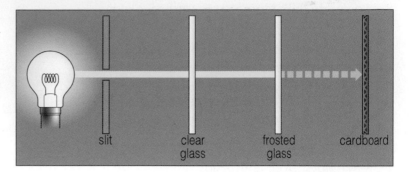

slit   clear glass   frosted glass   cardboard

Reflection is one way of changing the direction of a ray. Here is another way, using **refraction**.

Investigating refraction

Your teacher will give you a Help Sheet and a semi-circular block of glass (or perspex).

1 Place your block of glass in position on the Help Sheet, as shown here:

2 Use a ray-box to send a thin beam of light at an angle of incidence of 30°, as shown.

3 Look carefully at the ray where it comes out of the block.
Can you see the ray does not go straight on? It changes direction at the surface of the block. We say the ray is **refracted**. This is **refraction**.

4 Mark on the paper the path of the ray coming out of the block. Label it ray ①.

5 Now increase the angle of incidence to 40°. What happens?
Mark the new path of the refracted ray, and label it ②.

You can see that when light comes out of a glass block, it is bent (refracted) **away from** the normal line.

6 Now increase the angle of incidence to 50°. What happens now?
Mark the new path of the ray, and label it ③.

When the angle of incidence is large, you can see that the light is reflected **inside** the glass. We call this **total internal reflection**. This can be very useful, as you'll see on the next page.

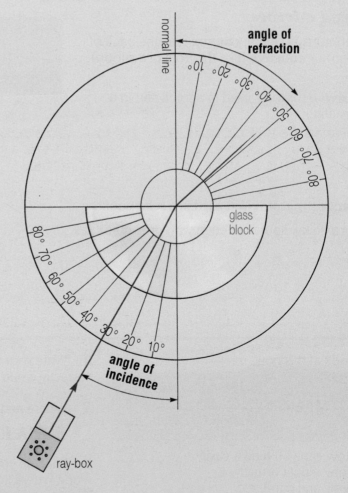

Using refraction

A **lens** is a shaped piece of glass. There are two kinds:

A **convex** lens is fat in the middle.
A **concave** lens is thin in the middle.

When light goes through a lens it is refracted.

A convex lens brings the rays of light closer together.
We say they are **converging**.

A concave lens makes the rays spread out. They are **diverging**.

The rays always bend towards the thickest part of a lens.

e Where is there a lens in your body?

f Is it convex or concave?

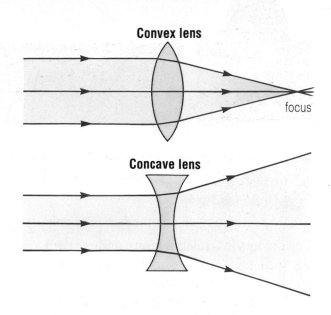

Convex lens

focus

Concave lens

Using total internal reflection

You discovered that light can be reflected **inside** your glass block.
This is used in the **cat's eye** reflector that you see on the roads.
The cat's eye is a triangular piece of glass, called a **prism**:

Light from a car head-lamp is reflected twice inside the prism, and then shines back into the driver's eye.

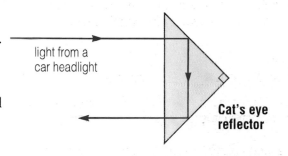

light from a
car headlight

**Cat's eye
reflector**

Doctors can use total internal reflection to see into your stomach.
They use a long thin piece of glass called an **optical fibre**.
The light is reflected from side to side along the glass fibre:

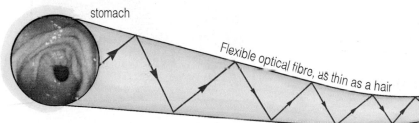

stomach

Flexible optical fibre, as thin as a hair

Things to do

1 Copy and complete:
a) When light goes in or out of glass, it . . . . direction. The rays are . . . . (bent). This is called . . . .
b) When light comes out of glass it is . . . . away from the normal line. When it goes into glass it is . . . . towards the normal.
c) In a convex lens the . . . . come closer together. The rays are . . . .
d) In a . . . . lens the rays spread out. They are . . . .
e) Total . . . . reflection is used in cat's eye . . . . and in . . . . fibres.

2 Look at the diagram of a **convex** lens at the top of this page.
Draw similar diagrams to show what you think would happen to the rays if the lens was: a) fatter, b) thinner.

3 Make a list of all the things you can think of that use a lens.

4 If you had an optical fibre several metres long, how could you use it to send messages to a friend in another room? What other uses can you think of?

8d   *A world of colour*

a Why do you think road signs are often coloured red?

b Imagine a world without colour. Describe what it would be like to live in it.

c Write down what you think are the colours in a rainbow.

The colours in a rainbow form a **spectrum**.

Making a spectrum

Shine some white light from a ray-box through a prism, and on to a screen:

Turn the prism until you see a spectrum on the screen.

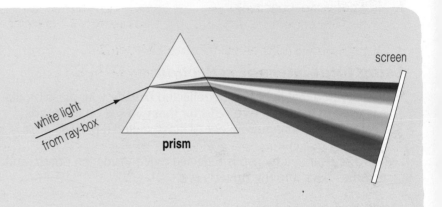

white light from ray-box

prism

screen

d How many different colours can you count?

e Which colour has been bent the least?

f Which colour has been refracted the most?

This experiment shows that white light is really a mixture of several colours. The colours are split up by the prism.

We say that the white light has been **dispersed** by the prism to form a visible spectrum. This is **dispersion**.

The colours, in order, are: **R**ed, **O**range, **Y**ellow, **G**reen, **B**lue, **I**ndigo, **V**iolet.
You can remember them as a boy's name: **ROY G. BIV**.

Light waves

If you throw a stone in a pond, you can see the ripples or **waves** spreading out from it.
Light spreads out in the same way, in waves.

Each wave has its own **wavelength**.
Different colours have different wavelengths.

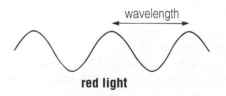

wavelength

red light

Red light has the longest wavelength. It is about $\frac{1}{1000}$ mm.

Violet light has the shortest wavelength. There are about 2000 wavelengths of violet light in 1 mm.

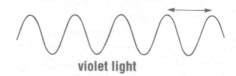

violet light

Seeing coloured objects

When light shines on a coloured object, some of the light is taken in or **absorbed**.
The rest of the light is reflected.
You see the colour of this reflected light. For example:

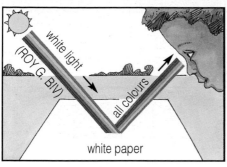

White things reflect all of the colours of light. That is, all of ROY G. BIV.

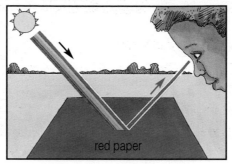

Red things reflect red light and absorb the other colours. We see the red light.

Black things do not reflect any light. All the light is absorbed.

g   What colour light is reflected by a blue T-shirt?

h   Explain what is happening when you look at this red ink.

Looking at objects in different colours of light

Plan an investigation that will give you the data for this table:

- To make the coloured light you can use a coloured **filter** on a ray-box (or torch).
  A red filter lets only red light through it.

- Show your plan to your teacher, and then do it.

- What pattern do you find?

Colour of objects in coloured lights

Colour of object in daylight	Colour of light shining on it			
	white	red	green	blue
white	white			
red				
green				
blue				

Colourful cars

Plan an investigation to see **which is the safest colour for a car**.
That is, which colour can be most easily seen in   a) daylight,
b) street lights, and
c) headlights.

Show your plan to your teacher, and if you have time, do it.

---

1   Copy and complete:
a)   . . . . light is a mixture of 7 colours.
b)   The 7 colours of the spectrum are:
c)   . . . . light has the longest wavelength.
d)   A red T-shirt reflects . . . . light and . . . . all the other colours.

2   What colour would a blue book look:
a)   in white light?   c)   in red light?
b)   in blue light?   d)   through a red filter?

3   Imagine you are in a rock band, and your stage lights usually flash red or blue. Design some clothes which will look good in red, in blue and in white light.
Draw colour pictures of what they will look like in: a)   white,   b)   red,   c)   blue light.

4   What is camouflage? Draw some camouflage suitable for a bird-watcher
a)   in the desert,   b)   in the jungle.

Things to do

Electromagnetic waves

8e

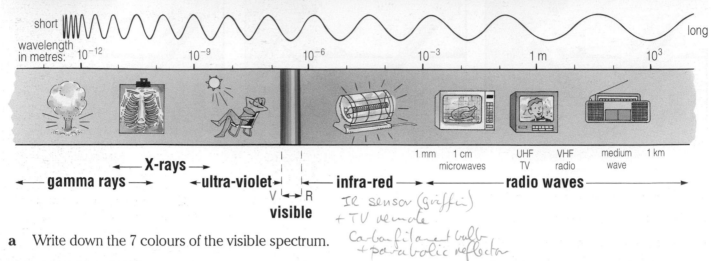

short ‖‖‖‖‖‖‖ wavelength in metres: 10^{-12} ... 10^{-9} ... 10^{-6} ... 10^{-3} ... 1 m ... 10^3 ... long

1 mm   1 cm   UHF   VHF   medium   1 km
microwaves   TV   radio   wave

← X-rays →
← gamma rays → ← ultra-violet → ← infra-red → ← radio waves →
V ↔ R
visible

*IR sensor (Griffin)
+ TV remote
Carbon filament bulb
+ parabolic reflector*

a Write down the 7 colours of the visible spectrum.

The spectrum you have seen is just a small part of a much bigger spectrum, called the **electromagnetic spectrum**. This is made of several different types of *radiation*.

The full electromagnetic spectrum is shown in the diagram above. Study it carefully.

b Write down the 6 main types of radiation, starting with gamma rays.

c Which type of radiation has the longest wavelength**?**

d Which type of radiation has the shortest wavelength**?**

Now use the data given on these two pages to answer questions **e** to **n**.

> **Electromagnetic waves:**
> 1 All can travel through empty space (a vacuum).
> 2 All travel at the same speed as light: 300 000 kilometres in every second.
> 3 All can be reflected and refracted.
> 4 They all transfer energy from one place to another.
> 5 The shorter the wavelength, the more dangerous they are.

Gamma rays (γ-rays) have the shortest wavelength. They are very penetrating and can pass right through metals.

They are given out by radio-active substances. They are very dangerous to humans unless used carefully.
Gamma rays are used to kill bacteria and sterilize hospital equipment.
With careful control they can be used to kill cancer cells. This is called radiotherapy:

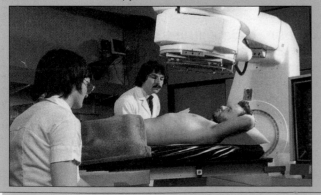

X-rays are very like gamma rays. They have a short wavelength.

X-rays are high-energy waves and are very penetrating. They can pass through skin easily, but not so easily through bones. Doctors and dentists use them to check bones and teeth:

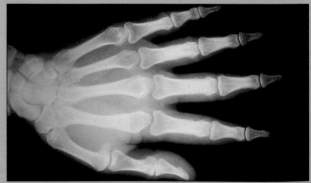

X-rays can be dangerous, because they can damage cells deep inside your body.
Pregnant women should avoid X-rays because they can damage the baby.

Ultra-violet rays (UV rays) come from the Sun and from sun-lamps. These are the waves that give you a sun-tan.

Ultra-violet rays damage your skin. They can cause skin cancer. This can be prevented by using sun-cream to block out the harmful rays.

UV can also be used to kill bacteria.

Infra-red rays (IR rays) are waves that are longer than red light. You cannot see IR rays but you can feel them on your skin as warmth.
Any warm or hot object gives out infra-red rays – including you!

cold · hot

Fire-fighters use infra-red detectors to look for people in smoke-filled rooms, and to find people buried alive after an earthquake.

e Which types of radiation cannot be seen by our eyes?

f Which rays are very like X-rays?

g Name a type of electromagnetic wave in each case:
i) Which can cause a sun-tan?
ii) Which can pass through metals?
iii) Which is emitted by warm objects?
iv) Which can be seen by your eye?

h Which waves are often used for communication?

i Are there radio waves in this room at the moment? How could you find out?

j How far do radio waves travel in 1 second?

k Which rays can be harmful to life?

l Write a newspaper article on sun-bathing. Discuss why people do it, and its dangers.

m Draw a poster to warn of the dangers of X-rays.

n Imagine you are an alien, just landed on Earth. Your eyes can only see with infra-red radiation. Describe what you might see as you leave your space-ship and walk through a town.

Radio waves have a longer wavelength. There are several kinds of radio waves:

Microwaves are used in microwave ovens. The energy of the microwaves heats up the food. Microwaves are also used for radar and for communicating with satellites.

UHF waves (**U**ltra **H**igh **F**requency) are used to transmit TV programmes to your home, and for mobile phones.

VHF waves (**V**ery **H**igh **F**requency) are used for local radio programmes, and by the police.

Medium wave and **long wave** radio are used to transmit over long distances.

1 Copy and complete:
a) The full electromagnetic spectrum, in order, is gamma rays, ..., ..., ..., ..., ...
b) .... waves have the longest wavelength.

2 Write down 5 things that electromagnetic waves have in common.

3 Cut out pictures from magazines to make a collage of the uses of different types of radiation.

4 Rattlesnakes have an extra pair of 'eyes' which see infra-red rays. Explain how this helps the snake to catch food. Why would the snake find it easier at night?

5 What do microwaves do to food? What materials can microwaves:
a) pass through?   b) not pass through?

6 Garry says that all 6 types of radiation are used somewhere in a hospital. Do you agree? Explain your answer.

Things to do

1 Design a lighting scheme for your bedroom. Show where you would put the lights, and where you might put some mirrors to make the room brighter.

2 Most animals have two eyes.
'Hunter' animals (like owls) have their eyes at the front of their heads.
'Hunted' animals (like rabbits) have theirs at the side of their heads.
Why do you think this is?

3 Look at your pen. Explain how you are able to see it.

4 Plan an investigation to see if snooker balls (or tennis balls) are reflected off a wall following the same rules as for light rays.
Draw a diagram and explain exactly how you would do it.

5 Can you find 6 consecutive letters in the alphabet that look the same when a mirror is placed to reflect half the letter?
Which other letters are symmetrical?

6 Draw a map of a sharp and dangerous bend in a road.
On the map show where you could place a mirror to make the bend safer for drivers.

7 A bike reflector is made of triangular pieces of red plastic.
It works like a cat's eye reflector.
a) Draw a diagram to show exactly how it reflects the light from the headlights of a car.
b) Why is the reflected light coloured red?

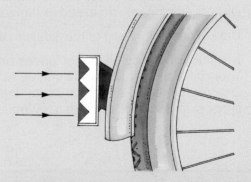

8 Make a colour survey of:
either the clothes in your wardrobe,
or the furnishings in your house,
or the cars on your street.
What is the best way to display your data?

9 Draw a poster warning people of the dangers of too much sun-bathing.

Sound

9

Sound is important to us. We need it to communicate with our friends.

Have you ever thought what it would be like not to be able to speak or hear?

This topic is about the nature of sound and how we use sound waves.

In this topic:

Sound moves

9a

▶ Sit quietly and just *listen*. Make a list of all the sounds you can hear in one minute.

▶ Write down as many 'sound' words as you can. For example, boom, bang, crash, squeak, . . .

▶ Touch the front of your throat while you make an 'aaah' sound. Can you feel it *vibrating*?

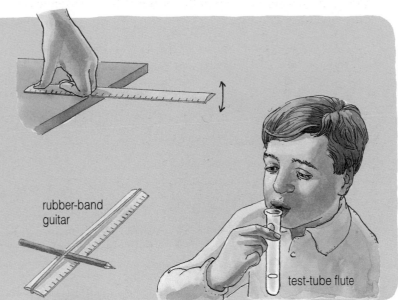

Hold a ruler firmly with part of it over the edge of the table. Then twang it.

a What is the end of the ruler doing?

b When does it stop making a sound?

c How can you make the sound quieter? How can you make it louder?

d How can you make it sound a higher note? And then a lower note? Can you play a tune – for example, 'Jingle Bells'?

Now repeat steps **a** to **d** with the other two 'musical instruments' shown here:

What do you find? Can you see any patterns? Write down your conclusions.

rubber-band guitar

test-tube flute

To make the ruler vibrate, you had to give it some *energy*.

e Where did this energy come from?

The vibrating ruler sends out sound waves through the air. Some of this sound energy travels to your ear, and so you can hear the sound.

Sound can travel a long way. In a thunderstorm, you can see a flash of lightning and then later you can hear the sound of it (the thunder).

f Which travels faster, light or sound?

Sound travels about 330 metres in one second. (Light travels almost a million times faster, at 300 000 000 metres per second.)

g How far would sound travel in 2 seconds?

h If you hear thunder 10 seconds after the lightning flash, how far away is the storm?

Echoes

If you clap your hands in front of a big building, you may hear an **echo**.

This happens because the sound wave is **reflected** back to you. The building is like a mirror.

Suppose you heard the echo after 2 seconds.

i How long did it take for the sound to get **to the wall?**

j How far away is the wall, if the speed of sound is 330 metres per second?

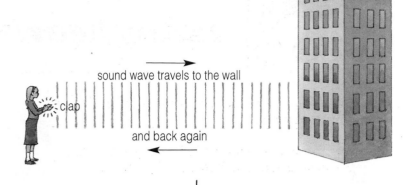

sound wave travels to the wall

clap

and back again

Echo-sounding

Sailors can use echoes to find the depth of the sea, using an **echo-sounder** or **sonar**.

Suppose this ship sent out a sound wave, and it got back an echo after 1 second.

k How long did it take the sound to get to the bottom of the sea?

Sound travels faster in water. It travels at 1500 metres per second.

l How far will the sound travel in $\frac{1}{2}$ second?

m How deep is the sea under the ship?

n If the shoal of fish in the diagram swims under the boat, how will the captain know?

The sound used by the sonar is too high for us to hear. It is called **ultrasonic** sound or **ultrasound**.

Dolphins use ultrasound to find their food. They make high-pitched squeaks and listen to the echoes.

Bats also use ultrasonic sounds, so that they can find food and 'see' in the dark.

▶ Plan an investigation to find the speed of sound.
- What equipment would you need?
- What measurements would you take?
- How would you calculate the speed?

---

1 Copy and complete:
a) All . . . . are caused by vibrations.
b) Echoes are due to the . . . . of sound.
c) The speed of sound in air is 330 . . . . per second.

2 Think about the noise in your school dining-hall. Write a list of suggestions for making it quieter.

3 Watching a cricket match from a distance, it seems that the bat hits the ball before you hear it. Explain this.

4 Karen hears an echo from a cliff after 4 seconds. How far is she from the cliff?

5 Write a poem using as many 'sound' words as possible.

Things to do

Hear, hear!

▶ Look at this diagram of your ear.
Study the different parts of it.

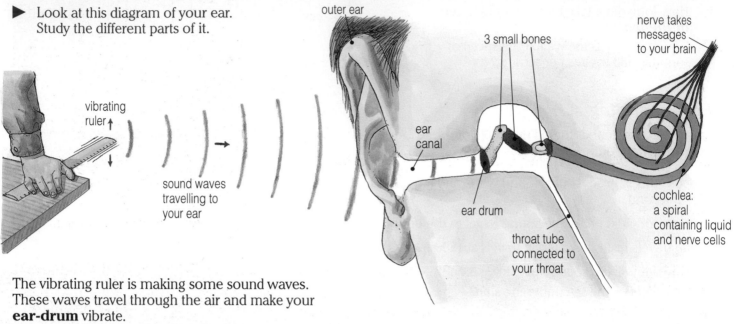

outer ear

3 small bones

nerve takes
messages
to your brain

ear
canal

ear drum

throat tube
connected to
your throat

cochlea:
a spiral
containing liquid
and nerve cells

vibrating
ruler

sound waves
travelling to
your ear

The vibrating ruler is making some sound waves.
These waves travel through the air and make your
ear-drum vibrate.
This makes the 3 small bones vibrate, and they make the liquid in
your **cochlea** vibrate. This affects the nerve cells in the cochlea and
a message is sent to your brain . . . and so you hear the sound.

▶ Your teacher will give you a copy of this diagram.
Fill in the missing words on it.

Looking after your ears

Your ear is very delicate and can easily be damaged.
This damage can cause deafness.

- Your ear canal can become blocked with wax. If
so, the doctor can wash it out.

- Your ear-drum can be torn by a very loud bang, or
damaged by an infection. It may mend itself, or
doctors can graft a new one.

- Your ear bones may stick together and stop
vibrating properly. An operation can fix this.

- Your 'middle ear' (the small bones and the throat
tube) may be infected. Antibiotics can cure this.

- Your cochlea can be damaged by loud noises – for
example, at pop concerts, near noisy machines, or
wearing 'walkman' headphones. There is *no* cure!

As people get older, their ears work less well. Partial
deafness can be helped by wearing a **hearing-aid**. It
amplifies the sound to make it louder.

Wearing 'ear defenders' at work

How does the size of your outer ear affect your hearing?

Investigate whether the size of the outer ear affects how well you can hear faint sounds.

You can make yourself larger 'ears' from card.

- What faint sounds will you try to hear?
- How can you carry out a fair test of different ear sizes?
- How will you record your results?
- How can you make your results more reliable?

Do your investigation. What do you find?

Does the *size* of the ear matter, or the *shape* of the ear, or both?

Sketch the shapes you have used.

Look at this bush-baby.
What conclusions can you make?

Are two ears better than one?

Investigate whether someone can tell the direction of a sound better with two ears or one.

- How will you make sure the person being tested uses only their ears?
- What will you use to make a sound?
- How will you make it a fair test?
- How will you record your results? Can you record them on a diagram or a map?

Show your plan to your teacher and then do it.

What do you find? Which is better: one ear or two?

Are people more accurate in some directions than others?

Write a report explaining what you did and what you found.

1 Someone plucks a guitar string and you hear it. Explain, step by step, what happens between the guitar string and your brain.

2 Design a poster to encourage teenagers to look after their ears better.

3 People sometimes cup their hands behind their ears when they are trying to hear. Explain why this helps, using all these words if you can:

vibrations	sound waves	
reflection	like a mirror	
concave	sound energy	ear

Things to do

Sound waves

▶ Look at the picture:

a Jan's throat is vibrating. Explain, step by step, how Mei hears the sound waves.

▶ Rabbits warn each other of danger by thumping the ground.

b Do you think sound can travel through a solid?

c How do whales 'talk' to each other?

d Can sound travel through water?

Sound travels

Use a 'slinky' spring to show how sound moves.

Push one end of the spring to compress it:

Then pull it back:

Then push it again, to compress it:

vibration

wave
This kind of wave is called a longitudinal wave.

You are ***vibrating*** the end of the spring.
A **wave** of energy travels down the spring.

You can see that some parts of the spring are pushed together, and other parts are pulled apart.

When you speak, sound energy travels from your mouth in the same way.
Instead of a spring, there are air particles called **molecules**.
When you speak, the molecules are pushed together and pulled apart, so that they vibrate like the spring.
The sound energy travels away from your mouth, like the wave on the spring. Sound travels 330 metres in every second.

Can sound travel through a vacuum?

e What is a vacuum?

Your teacher will show you what happens to sound when the air is removed from a bell-jar:

f First, ***predict*** what you expect to happen.

g What happens as the air is pumped out?

h What happens as the air is let back in?

i Explain this experiment.

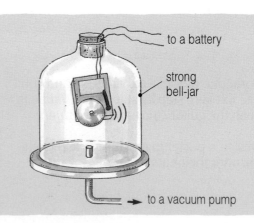

to a battery

strong
bell-jar

to a vacuum pump

What notes can you hear?

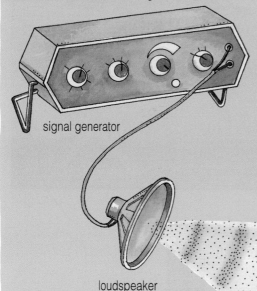

signal generator

loudspeaker

Your teacher will connect a **signal generator** to a **loudspeaker**. The signal generator makes the loudspeaker vibrate, so that it makes a sound wave.

The dial on the signal generator tells you the **frequency** of the vibration. The frequency is measured in **hertz** (also written as **Hz**).

If the frequency is 100 Hz, the loudspeaker is vibrating 100 times in every second. This gives you a low note, like a bass guitar. We say it has a low **pitch**.

- Turn the knob on the signal generator to a higher frequency.
- **j** What happens to the pitch of the note?
- **k** What is the highest frequency you can hear?
- **l** What is the lowest frequency you can hear?

- Now connect a **microphone** to a **cathode ray oscilloscope** (**CRO**).

  A CRO is a special TV set. It shows you the **wave-form** of the sound wave.

- Look at the wave-form as you change the frequency (pitch) of the sound.

- **m** Sketch the wave-form when the sound has a high frequency. Label it.

- **n** Do the same with a low frequency sound.

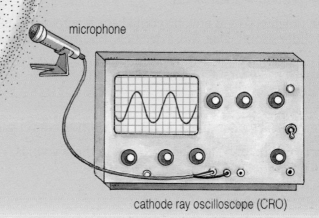

microphone

cathode ray oscilloscope (CRO)

▶ The diagram shows the hearing range of some animals:

o What do you notice?

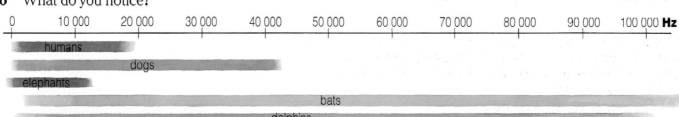

| 0 | 10 000 | 20 000 | 30 000 | 40 000 | 50 000 | 60 000 | 70 000 | 80 000 | 90 000 | 100 000 **Hz** |

humans
dogs
elephants
bats
dolphins

---

1 Copy and complete:
a) Sound can travel through solids, ... , and gases.
b) Sound cannot travel through a . . . .
c) In a sound wave, the tiny . . . . are pushed together and pulled farther apart.
d) The frequency of a vibration is measured in . . . . This is also written . . . .
e) A note with a high pitch has a high . . . .
f) The human range of hearing is from about 20 Hz up to about . . . . Hz.

2 Why can't sound travel:
a) in a vacuum?   b) on the Moon?

3 Sound travels at different speeds in different materials:

Material	air	water	wood	iron
Speed of sound (m/s)	330	1500	4000	5000

a) Plot a bar-chart of this information.
b) What pattern can you see?

Things to do

9d Noise annoys

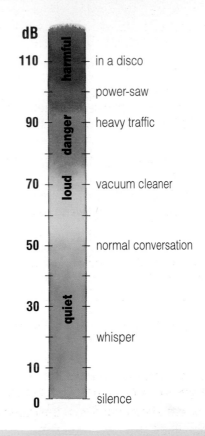

▶ What do you think is the difference between *music* and *noise*?

a Write down 3 words to describe music.
b Write down 3 words to describe noise.

Noise is any sound that we don't like. It is a kind of pollution.

c Give 3 examples of sounds that are noise to you.

The loudness of any sound is measured in **decibels**. This is often written as **dB**.

The quietest sound anyone could hear is zero decibels (0 dB). A louder sound, with more decibels, has more *energy*.

The scale shows the loudness of different sounds:

d What is the loudness, in dB, of a normal conversation?

Try to estimate the loudness (in dB) of these sounds,
e birds singing,
f a food-mixer.

Loud sounds are dangerous. They can make you permanently deaf.

g If you were using a power-saw, what should you wear?

h Why is it often dangerous in a disco?

i Why does the noise in a sports hall sound loud?
j *Why* would it change if there was a carpet and curtains?

dB		
110	harmful	in a disco
		power-saw
90	danger	heavy traffic
70	loud	vacuum cleaner
50		normal conversation
30	quiet	
		whisper
10		
0		silence

Investigating sound-levels

Use a sound-level meter to measure the loudness of some sounds:

Show your results on a scale like the one above.

Using a sound-level meter   Wearing ear-defenders at work

Noisy neighbours

Kelly's neighbours are very noisy. The noise comes through the walls while Kelly is doing her homework. She wants to make the walls of her bedroom sound-proof.

Plan an investigation to find out **which material is best for making sounds quieter**.

- Your teacher will give you several materials.
  For example: paper, kitchen foil, foam rubber, cloth, polythene bag, plasticine, sellotape, cotton wool, etc.

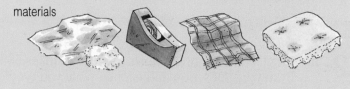

materials

- **Predict** which material you think will be best.
  Can you explain why?

- You will need something to make the sound.
  For example: a clock or a buzzer, or a tin-can containing stones, or a radio, or your voice.

sources

- You will need something to detect how much sound gets through the material.
  For example: your ear, or a sound-level meter, or a microphone and CRO.

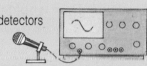

detectors

- Plan what you are going to do. How will you make it a **fair test**?
- How will you record your results?
- Show your plan to your teacher, and then do it.

- Write a report for Kelly, explaining which material is best for sound-proofing her room.

- Which sorts of materials are best? Is there any pattern in your results?

- How could you improve your test?

Imagine you live on a very busy road, with a lot of traffic noise.
In your group, discuss these questions:

k How could you cut down the traffic noise in your garden?

l How could you cut down traffic noise inside your house?

m What do you think should be done to reduce traffic noise in towns?

Things to do

1 Copy and complete:
a) The loudness of a sound is measured in . . . . (often written as . . . .).
b) A louder sound has more . . . .

2 Design a poster to encourage teenagers to be more considerate to deaf people.

3 Imagine you are working in a noisy office. What suggestions could you make to improve it?

4 You are looking out of the window, in a dark room, drinking a cup of coffee, and with the TV on. A deaf person comes into the room. What things would you do before speaking to her?

5 Dave says, "I can work better on my homework if I have some music playing." Wayne says, "I don't agree – the music will spoil your concentration."
Plan an investigation to see who is right.

Questions

1 Explain in your own words how a bat can find its way in the dark.

2 a) Imagine, in a thunderstorm, lightning strikes 660 metres away from you. Describe and explain what you would observe. (The speed of sound in air is 330 metres per second.)
   b) A fighter plane flies at a speed of Mach 4. The speed of sound is called Mach 1. How fast is the plane flying?

3 Plan an investigation to see if children have better hearing than adults. How would you make it a fair test?

4 Carry out a sound survey among your family and friends. Make a list of everyone's favourite and least favourite sounds.

5 a) Copy out the table. Tick a column to show if the frequency is a high or a low pitch.
   b) Older people cannot hear very high notes. Why do you think your range of hearing will get smaller as you get older?
   c) What is ultra-sound? How do bats use it?

Frequency	Pitch	
	high	low
10 000 Hz		
50 Hz		
50 kHz		
20 kHz		

6 Alan, Bev and Claire have read that people find high frequency sounds more annoying than low frequency sounds. They each have a hypothesis:

Alan says, "I think it's because high frequency sounds make it harder to hear someone talking."

Bev says, "I think it's because our ears are more sensitive to high-pitched sounds."

Claire says, "I think it's because high frequency sounds can penetrate through walls more easily."

a) Do you agree with any of these hypotheses?
b) Choose one, and plan an investigation to test it.

Food and Digestion

You need food to live.
Your food gives you your energy.
Without the right sort of food you won't grow strong and healthy.

In this topic you will find out what happens to your food when it is broken down inside your body.

Food for thought

10a

Do you have any favourite foods?

▶ Make a list of some of the foods that you like to eat.

Which of these foods do you think are good for you?

Draw a ring around those foods that are not good for you.

Healthy eating

You need a healthy diet to:
- grow • repair damaged cells • get energy • keep healthy.

A healthy diet should include some of each of these:

Proteins are for growth. They are used to make new cells and repair damaged tissue.

Carbohydrates, like sugar and starch, are our high-energy foods, but eat too much and they turn to fat.

Fats are used to store energy. They also insulate our bodies so that we do not lose a lot of heat.

Vitamins and minerals are needed in small amounts to keep us healthy e.g. iron for the blood and vitamin D for the bones.

The easiest way to have a healthy diet is to eat a variety of foods each day.

▶ Choose one food from each picture to plan some healthy meals.

▶ Look at the newspaper report:

a What is meant by 'junk food' or 'fast food'?

b Why do you think a lot of children eat junk or fast food
i) at home? ii) in school?

c Why is it important to eat fresh fruit and vegetables?

Survey shows junk food is favourite

Kids ditch salad for the chips

JUNK food is children's first love at lunchtime, a survey disclosed today.

Pizzas, burgers and hot dogs are top of the menu for school dinners, with pupils giving scarcely a second thought to healthy eating.

Fresh fruit is losing out to junk food. Children eat only 60% of the fruit they did 4 years ago.

Food tests

Here are 4 ways of testing for foods.

Do each test carefully and observe the result.

Write down your results in each case.

Testing for starch

Add 2 drops of *iodine* solution to some starch solution.

What do you see?

 eye protection

Testing for glucose

Add 10 drops of **Benedict's solution** to one-third of a test-tube of glucose solution.

Heat carefully in a water bath.

What do you see?

 eye protection

Testing for protein

Add 10 drops of **Biuret solution** (be careful: this is corrosive) to half a test-tube of protein solution.

What do you see?

 eye protection

Testing for fat

Rub some of the food onto a piece of filter paper.

Hold the paper up to the light.

What do you see?

Alcohol goes cloudy with fat

Now try testing a few foods. If the food is a solid you will have to grind it up with a little water first.

Record your results in a table like this:

Food	Starch	Glucose	Protein	Fat
Nuts			✓	✓

Things to do

1   Copy and complete the table:

Food	Use to my body	Food containing a lot of it	Chemical test
protein starch fat glucose			

2   Do some research to find out what these vitamins and minerals are needed for. What happens if you do not get enough of them?
a) vitamin C   d) calcium
b) iron   e) vitamin B group
c) vitamin A   f) iodine.

3   Your teacher will give you a table of Recommended Daily Amounts of nutrients (RDAs). Keep a careful record of all the food that you eat in the next 24 hours.
Use the Recommended Daily Amounts table to see if you had a healthy diet.

4   Fibre or roughage is an essential part of your diet. Do some research to find out
a) what fibre is   b) where it is found
c) why it is so important to us.

Teeth and decay

10b

Do you have healthy teeth?
They make your mouth look good and feel good.
Your teeth are important and you should remember to take care of them.
They chew your food up into small pieces before you swallow it.
Imagine trying to swallow an apple whole!

a Which foods could you eat if you had no teeth?

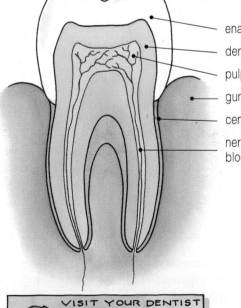

molars

pre-molars

canine

incisors

Types of teeth

▶ Look at your teeth in a mirror.

When you are an adult you should have 32, but you won't have all of them yet!

Look carefully for the 4 types of teeth.

b Write down what you think each of them is used for.

▶ Your teacher will give you a diagram of a set of teeth.

Shade in the ones in which you have fillings and cross out any that are missing.

Parts of a tooth

The part of a tooth that you can see in your mouth is covered with a white layer of **enamel**.
Enamel is the hardest substance in your body.

c Why is it found here?

Underneath is the living part of your tooth which is made of **dentine**. This is softer than enamel.

In the middle of each tooth is the **pulp cavity** which contains nerves and blood vessels.

d When you have a tooth out, why does it bleed and feel sore?

Do you brush your teeth properly?
▶ Find out about how you should brush your teeth.
Your teacher can give you a Help Sheet.

Remember, you can keep your teeth and gums healthy by:

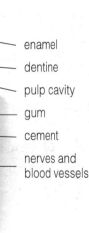

enamel

dentine

pulp cavity

gum

cement

nerves and blood vessels

CLEAN YOUR TEETH at least TWICE A DAY
after breakfast and before going to bed!

REPLACE YOUR TOOTHBRUSH
when it wears out
every 4-6 months

AVOID SUGARY FOOD & DRINK
Between meals

VISIT YOUR DENTIST REGULARLY EVERY 6 MONTHS

Under attack

Tooth decay can spoil your looks and cause pain.
Before brushing, do your teeth feel rough and sticky in places?
This is **plaque**. It can form when food sticks to the surface of your teeth.

1 Bacteria grow on the food (especially sugary food) and form plaque.

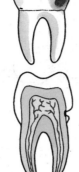

3 Food collects in the cavity and bacteria make more acid. This acid attacks the enamel and the cavity gets bigger.

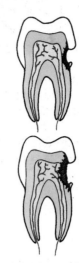

2 The bacteria make acid. This acid attacks the enamel and makes a small hole (a **cavity**).

4 Once through the enamel the cavity quickly spreads through the dentine to the pulp. The nerve is now affected. It can be very painful.

Plaque attack

How effective are different toothpastes at killing bacteria?

1 Take an agar plate with harmless bacteria growing on it.
2 Use a marker pen to write 4 numbers on the underside of your plate, in the positions shown in the diagram.
3 Use tweezers to pick up a filter paper disc and dab it on some toothpaste.
4 Lift the lid and with tweezers carefully place the paper disc onto the agar. Make sure the side of the disc with toothpaste on is in contact with the agar.
5 Repeat this for 3 different toothpastes making a note of each one's number.
6 Replace the lid and fix it down with adhesive tape.
7 Place your agar plate in a warm incubator at 25 °C for 2 days.
8 Wash your hands with soap and warm water.
9 After 2 days, measure the diameter of any clear areas. Sketch your results on a copy of the diagram.
   Do not open the plate.
   When you have finished, return the plate to your teacher.

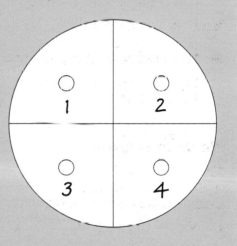

e What effects do the different toothpastes have on the bacteria?
f Which toothpaste do you think is best to use and why?
g Many toothpastes are alkaline. How does this help them fight tooth decay?

---

1 Copy and complete:
The hard coating on the outside of a tooth is called . . . . It surrounds a softer layer called . . . . In the middle of the tooth is the pulp . . . . which contains . . . . vessels and . . . .

2 If fluoride is added, in small amounts, to drinking water, it can reduce tooth decay. In large amounts fluoride can be poisonous to humans. Carry out a survey to find out what people think about this problem.

3 Take half a raw carrot and use it to find out what each type of tooth does. Nibble or gnaw off a small piece, then bite off a larger one. Tear off a piece like a dog tears meat. Finally chew it and grind it up for swallowing. Record how each of your teeth is used.

4 Suppose you have to give a 2-minute talk to some junior school children about caring for their teeth. Write down what you would say.

Things to do

Digestion

10c

Think of the different foods that you eat.
How much of your food is **soluble** (will dissolve in water)?
Probably not much.

Before our bodies can use the food that we eat it must be **digested**.
When food is digested it is broken down into very small molecules:

There are special **digestive juices** in our body.
These digest large molecules into small ones.

▶ Try chewing some bread for a long time. Eventually it tastes sweet
because your saliva has broken down the starch in the bread to sugar.

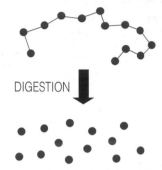

Starch is a very big molecule. It is made up
of lots of sugar molecules joined together.

DIGESTION

sugar molecules are very small

How enzymes work

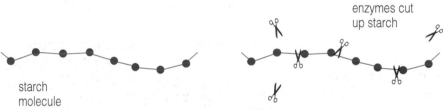

enzymes cut
up starch

starch
molecule

sugar molecules

Saliva contains a chemical called an **enzyme**.
This acts like scissors to cut up the starch molecule into sugar
molecules.

Proteins are large food molecules.
They are made up of small **amino acids** joined together.

Fats are large food molecules.
They are made up of small **fatty acids** joined together.

a What do you think happens to proteins and fats in digestion?
You could draw simple diagrams to help your explanation.

Enzymes can be very particular.
For instance, the enzyme in saliva will only digest starch.
It will not digest protein or fat.
Similarly it takes a different enzyme to digest protein and another
one to digest fat.
For this reason we say that enzymes are *specific*.

Changing starch into sugar

You can find out how saliva affects starch by carrying out this experiment.

1 Set the 2 test-tubes up as shown in the diagram.
2 Leave the apparatus for 10 minutes at 40 °C.
3 Test a drop from each test-tube for starch with iodine. What do you see?
4 Add some Benedict's solution to each test-tube and test for sugar. What do you see?
5 Record your results in a table like this:

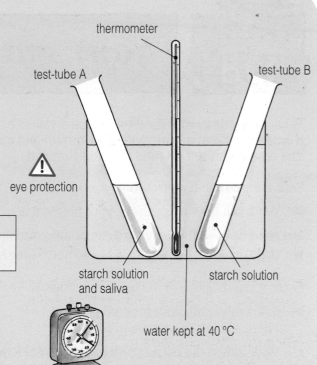

	Colour with iodine	Colour with Benedict's
test-tube A test-tube B		

b In which test-tube was the starch broken down?
c What do you think the starch was broken down to?
d Why do you think test-tube B contained only starch solution?
e Why were your test-tubes kept at 40 °C?

Why digest?

Food must be broken down and made soluble in your body. This is so that it can pass through your gut wall into your blood. Your blood then carries the digested food all around your body.

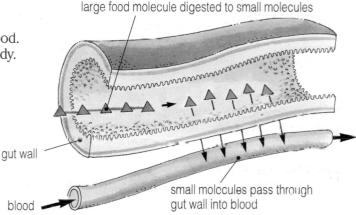

f Why can't undigested food pass through your gut wall into your blood?
g Which parts of your body need the food?
h In what ways does your body 'use up' food?

Fibre cannot be digested so it isn't broken down.
Fibre adds bulk and a solid shape to your food so that it can be pushed along your gut.
Tough, stringy plants like celery have lots of fibre.

▶ Make a list of foods that are high in fibre.

---

1 Copy and complete:
Digestion is the . . . . down of food into . . . . molecules by chemicals called . . . . Food has to be digested so that it can pass through the . . . . wall into the . . . . stream. Starch is digested to . . . ., protein is digested to . . . . acids, and fats are digested to . . . . acids.

2 Biological washing powders contain enzymes. Many stains contain fat and protein that can be digested by enzymes. Plan an investigation into the effect of temperature on biological and non-biological washing powders.

3 The graph shows the effect of temperature on the activity of an enzyme.
a) At what temperature is the enzyme most active?
b) Explain what is happening to the action of the enzyme i) between X and Y ii) between Y and Z.

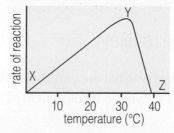

Things to do

Your gut

What happens to your food when you swallow?
It enters a tube that starts with your mouth and ends at your anus.
The whole of this food tube is called your **gut**.

Your gut is about 9 metres long.

▶ Work out how many times your height it is.

a How does all this length of gut fit into your body?

b Why do you think your gut has to be so long?

Look at the diagram of the human gut below.

▶ Follow the path your food goes down.
  There are lots of twists and turns.

c Write down the correct order of parts that food passes through.

Down the tube

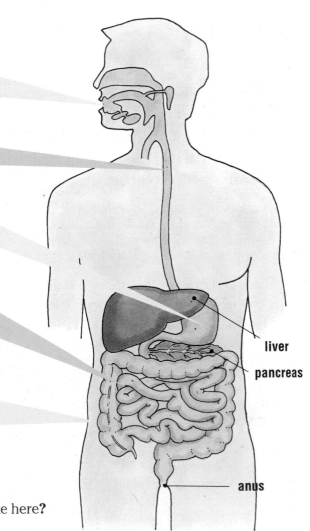

Mouth
Food chewed and mixed with saliva.
Then you swallow it (gulp!).
(Food is here for 20 seconds)

Gullet
A straight, muscular tube leading to your stomach.
(10 seconds)

Stomach
The acid bath! Digestive juices and acid are added to food here. Your stomach churns up this mixture.
(2 to 6 hours)

Small intestine
More juices are added from your liver and your pancreas.
These complete digestion. Then the food passes through into your blood. This is called **absorption**.
(About 5 hours)

Large intestine
Only food that can not be digested (like fibre) reaches here.
A lot of water passes back into your body. This leaves solid waste to pass through your anus.
(Up to 24 hours)

liver

pancreas

anus

d In which part of your gut does food stay the longest?
  Why do you think this is?

e Proteins are digested in your stomach. What are conditions like here?

f How long does it take food to pass down the whole length of your gut?

A model gut

You can make a model gut using **Visking tubing**.

1 Wash the Visking tubing in warm water to soften it.
2 Tie one end in a tight knot.
3 Use a syringe to fill the tubing with 5 cm^3 of starch solution and 5 cm^3 of glucose solution.
4 Wash the outside of the tubing.
5 Support your model gut in a boiling tube with an elastic band.
6 Fill the boiling tube with water and leave for 15 minutes.
7 After 15 minutes, test the water for starch and for sugar.

⚠️ eye protection

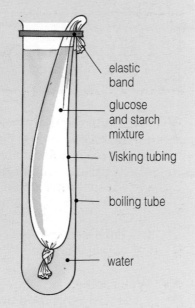

elastic band
glucose and starch mixture
Visking tubing
boiling tube
water

g Which food passed through the tubing into the water?
h Which food did not pass through the tubing into the water?
i Which part of the apparatus was like: i) food in your gut? ii) your gut wall? iii) the blood around your gut?

Getting through

j How do you think food molecules pass through the Visking tubing?

k Which food molecule (**A** or **B**) is starch and which one is glucose?

l Which food molecule (**A** or **B**) will pass through the Visking tubing?

m Which food molecule, starch or glucose, will pass easily through the wall of your small intestine?

n What would have to happen to food molecule **B** before it could pass through the Visking tubing?

o How do you think this could happen?

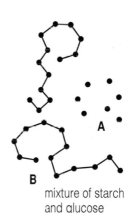

A
B
mixture of starch and glucose inside

---

1 Match the parts of the body in the first column with the descriptions in the second column:

a) stomach
b) small intestine
c) large intestine
d) mouth
e) gullet

i) most water is absorbed here.
ii) saliva is made here.
iii) most food is absorbed here.
iv) carries food down to the stomach.
v) is very acidic.

2 Find out how each of the following parts of the body help digestion to take place:
a) liver   b) pancreas   c) appendix.

3 The following are diseases of the gut:
a) constipation   b) stomach ulcers   c) diarrhoea.
Find out the causes of each of these diseases.

Things to do

Questions

1 The graph shows the activity of 2 enzymes: amylase and pepsin.
a) At which pH does pepsin work best?
b) Pepsin is made in the stomach. How does the stomach keep its pH just right for pepsin to work best?
c) Pepsin breaks down proteins. What will be formed as a result?
d) At what pH does amylase work best?
e) Amylase breaks down starch. What will be formed as a result?
f) Amylase works in your mouth. Why is it useful that saliva contains an alkali?

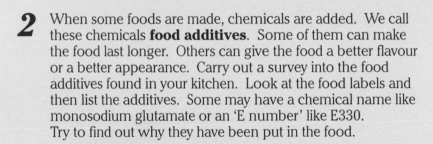

2 When some foods are made, chemicals are added. We call these chemicals **food additives**. Some of them can make the food last longer. Others can give the food a better flavour or a better appearance. Carry out a survey into the food additives found in your kitchen. Look at the food labels and then list the additives. Some may have a chemical name like monosodium glutamate or an 'E number' like E330. Try to find out why they have been put in the food.

3 Plan an investigation to compare the amount of water in a piece of plant food with the amount of water in a piece of meat. You can use the sort of apparatus found in your science laboratory. Remember to make it a fair test and check your plan with your teacher before carrying it out.

4 Visit your local supermarket. Find out the cost of different food groups using the examples in the table:
a) Which food can you buy most of for £5?
b) Which food can you buy least of for £5?

Some families have more to spend on food than others.
c) Which food groups do you think a family on a very low income would have to buy, to feed themselves?
d) Which food groups would a high-income family be able to buy?
e) Do you think your answers to c) and d) would be true in India and in the United States?

Food group	Example	Cost per 1 kg
carbohydrates	potatoes rice	
fats	cheese butter	
proteins	chicken lamb	
vitamins and minerals	oranges broccoli	

5 For this question you will need a table of Recommended Daily Amounts of nutrients (RDAs).
a) Write down how much energy you need. How does this compare with:
  i) a 1-year-old?
  ii) someone the same age as you but of the opposite sex?
  iii) a very active adult female?
b) Which group shows the biggest increase in protein needs for each sex? Why do you think this is?
c) Which foods does a pregnant woman need more of than a female desk worker? Try to explain these differences.

6 Plan the following meals, choosing foods that would be good for you:
a) A good breakfast for a 12-year-old.
b) A high-energy lunch for an athlete before a big race.
c) An evening meal low in fat but rich in fibre and protein.

Acids and alkalis

11

Have you heard of acids and alkalis?
What do you know about them already?

These substances are important to us in everyday life. They are used to make clothes, paints, soaps, fertilisers, medicines and many other things.

There are even acids and alkalis inside your body!
Your stomach wall makes acid. If too much acid is made, it can be a problem. In this topic you can find out how to solve the problem.

You might also think about the 'hydrangea plant mystery'. How can you make the plant grow blue flowers this year … and pink flowers next year?

In this topic:

A question of acid or alkali

▶ Write down 5 words that come to mind when you hear the word **acid**.

▶ What do you think an acid is?
You could use some of your 5 words to help you write a sentence.
I think an acid is …

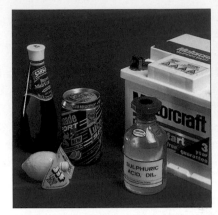

All these contain acids

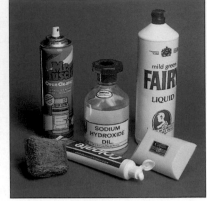

All these contain alkalis

▶ Think of as many examples as you can of opposites, e.g. big/small.

Acids and **alkalis** are *chemical* opposites.

Indicators can be used to show which things are acids and which things are alkalis.

Have you ever used **litmus** indicator?
Litmus is a useful indicator. It can be in the form of a paper or a liquid. It is a purple dye which turns *red* in acid and *blue* in alkali.

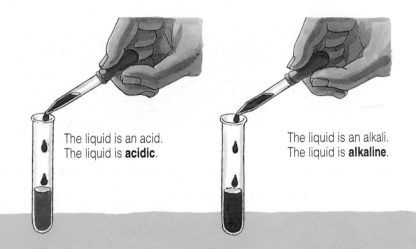

The liquid is an acid.
The liquid is **acidic**.

The liquid is an alkali.
The liquid is **alkaline**.

Making your own indicators

Some brightly coloured berries, flower petals and vegetables make good indicators.

Look at the pictures to see how you can make your own indicator.

plant pieces

pestle

mortar

methylated spirit

⚠️ flammable

Crush your plant pieces.

Add a little methylated spirit.

Keep crushing until all the colour has come out.

Use a pipette to put the liquid into a test-tube.

You can use this method to make some indicators for the next investigation.

Which indicator is the best?

In your group discuss what makes a good indicator.

Make a list of your ideas.

Use these ideas to find out which of the petals, fruits or berries makes the best indicator. Remember you will need to do fair tests.

How can you make your results reliable?

Use the method shown on the opposite page to make your own indicators.

When you have made your indicators your teacher can give you some acids and alkalis for your tests.

Write a report on what you did.

Which was the best indicator?

How could you improve your investigation?

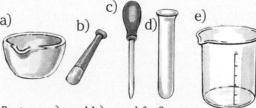

It's a fact!

Drivers who transport acids and alkalis must carry **Tremcards**. This stands for Transport Emergency Cards. The cards tell the driver what to do if there is an emergency.

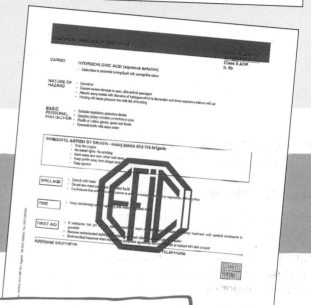

---

1 Copy the sentences below into your book filling in the blanks.
Acids are the chemical opposites of . . . .
Indicators are one . . . . in acids and another . . . . in alkalis.
Litmus is a useful indicator. It turns red in . . . . and blue in . . . .

2 What do all the alkalis in the picture at the top of the opposite page have in common?

3 On the Tremcard for dilute hydrochloric acid the emergency action for a spillage is:

- Drench with water
- If the substance has entered a sewer advise police

Why do you think it says this on the Tremcard?

4 Name these pieces of apparatus.

a) b) c) d) e)

What are a) and b) used for?

5 Write explanations for the following:
a) bottles of hydrochloric acid have warning labels
b) bottles of lemon juice do not have warning labels
c) acids are usually kept in glass bottles, not in metal containers.

6 Think about the practical work you did in today's lesson. Make a list of things you did well. Make a list of things you didn't do well. Write down 2 things you could improve next time.

Things to do

How strong?

▶ Crack the code to find out what you will be asked to do today!

Take:

- The second letter of the word: A rainbow has 7 of these.
- The first letter of the word: The colour of litmus with an alkali.
- The first letter of the word: You wash your hands with this.
- The second letter of the word: An acid you put on pancakes.
- The last letter of the word: It detects acids and alkalis.
- The first letter of the word: An acid served on chips.
- The second letter of the word: The colour of litmus with an acid.

You can use indicators to test for acids and alkalis.

Universal indicator is a mixture of a few indicators. It is very useful because it tells you how ***strong*** or how ***weak*** the acids and alkalis are. You can get universal indicator as a liquid or as paper.

Testing acids and alkalis

Your teacher will give you some solutions to test.

Put one of the solutions in a test-tube (about a quarter full).

Add a few drops of universal indicator. Shake this tube carefully. What do you see?

Use the colour chart to find the **pH number** of your solution.

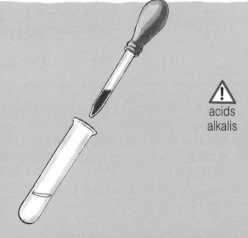

⚠ acids alkalis

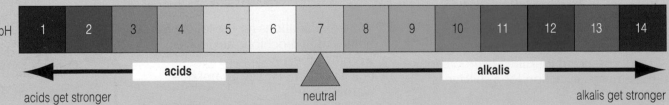

pH: 1 2 3 4 5 6 7 8 9 10 11 12 13 14

◀ acids ▲ alkalis ▶

acids get stronger   neutral   alkalis get stronger

Test the other solutions with universal indicator.

Write down the ***colour*** and ***pH number*** each time. Record whether the solution is an acid or an alkali.

Which is the strongest acid?
Which is the strongest alkali?

Substance	Colour	pH	Acid or alkali?
		·	

Acid rain

Homework

Have you heard about the **acid rain** problem? When fuels burn they make gases which move into the air. These gases are made of acids – they are acidic. The gases dissolve in water in the clouds. When it rains the acids are brought back to earth. Acid rain can damage buildings and trees. It affects our **environment**.

Stonework damaged by acid rain

Trees damaged by acid rain

Carry out this investigation to see how acid rain affects stonework.

Add a few drops of acid to some crushed limestone.
Write down what you see.

What do you think would happen if you used a weaker acid?
Write down what you expect to see.

Now try it with the weaker acid.

Was your prediction correct?

Do you think acid rain is a strong or weak acid? Why?

acid

acid

crushed limestone

watch glass

Things to do

1 Match each of these pH numbers with the correct statement.

pH6	strong acid
pH1	strong alkali
pH14	weak acid
pH8	weak alkali

2 Copy and complete this sentence. Universal indicator is more useful than litmus because …

3 Answer the following questions about acid rain.
a) Look at the photograph at the top of this page and describe what acid rain does to trees.
b) Write down 3 ways in which humans could make less acid rain
c) Look at your answer to b). Draw a poster to get the message across.

4 Kate says "I think milk gets more acidic if it is left out of the fridge for a long time." Do you think it is right? Plan an investigation to test Kate's idea.

5 How could you use the crushed limestone and acid test to put 4 acids in order of their strength?

A balancing act

▶ Look back to the pH chart. Find the pH number of a solution which is neither acidic nor alkaline.

a What colour is universal indicator in this solution?

I think it's an acid.

Solutions which are neither acids nor alkalis are **neutral**.

You can make neutral solutions by mixing acids and alkalis together. The acid and alkali can balance each other out.

ACID + ALKALI → NEUTRAL SOLUTION

I think it's an alkali.

▶ Copy the diagrams below into your book. The 3 labels are missing. Choose the correct labels from the list to complete your diagrams.

- water
- acid
- acid and indicator
- alkali
- neutral solution and indicator
- indicator
- neutral solution
- alkali and indicator

Neutralising your stomach!

Did you know that there is acid in your stomach?

Have you ever had a stomach ache? Sometimes this can be caused by your stomach making too much acid.

Indigestion tablets or stomach powders can be used to 'settle' your stomach.

Do you think these tablets and powders are acids, alkalis or neutral? Why?

▶ Have you seen any advertisements about curing indigestion?

Write down the names of some cures.

SCI-CO HEALTHCARE

Your health is our care

MEMO TO: *Analysts*   FROM: *Chris Williams*

The company wishes to test three stomach powders, A, B and C, to see how well they neutralise stomach acid.

Please carry out some tests to tell me how much of each powder you need to neutralise the stomach acid. Make sure you do fair tests. Be as accurate as possible.

Our first tests show that one powder will not work at all. Please check this. I'd like a report on:

(a) how you carried out the tests - including all measurements you made

(b) your results

(c) which powder is best at neutralising stomach acid.

This is urgent! Thanks.

Things to do

1 Copy and complete:
A substance with a . . . . number of 4 is an . . . . If a weak . . . . is added to it, the solution can become neutral with a pH number of . . . .

2 Acid can cause tooth decay! Design and make a leaflet to tell young children about the need to brush teeth regularly.

3 In the last few lessons you have been using different indicators – litmus, universal indicator, and some you made yourself from petals, berries or vegetables.
Why is universal indicator the best one to use when neutralising acids or alkalis?

4 Find out about some medicines used to treat stomach acid and indigestion.
a) Make a list of their ingredients.
b) Are there any chemicals in common? If so, give their names.
c) List the names of the medicines in a table like this.

Tablet	Powder	Liquid

d) Medicines can be sold as tablets, powder or liquid.
Write down an advantage of each of these.
e) What other things would you consider before choosing a medicine to cure indigestion?

11d

pH is pretty Helpful

pH in the garden

The pH of a soil is very important. Some plants grow well in acidic soil. Some would grow better in neutral or alkaline soil.

Gardeners and farmers need to know the pH of their soil. The soil gets too acidic sometimes. This can stop plants growing well. The farmers could add lime (an alkali) to change the pH of the soil.

It's a fact!

You can buy pH test kits from garden centres to test your own soil.

Testing soils

Your teacher will give you some different soils to test.

Take your first soil sample and put 2 spatula measures in a test-tube. Add about 5 cm^3 of distilled water. Stopper the tube and shake it for about a minute.

Set up a filter funnel and paper. Filter the soil mixture into another test-tube. Add universal indicator to the filtrate. Record the pH value.

Repeat this test with other soils.

soil and distilled water
filter paper
filter funnel
soil
filtrate

Soil sample	pH value
A	
B	
.	
.	
.	

Write down answers to the following questions.

a Why do you use **distilled** water in the test?

b Why do you 'shake for about a minute'?

c Which soil is the most acidic?

d Which soil is the most alkaline?

Look at the plant pH preference list (opposite) from the pH test kit.

e Which of your soil samples do you think could grow
(i) apples (ii) potatoes (iii) blackcurrants?

f Which crops could soil A grow?

Plant pH preference	
Name	pH preference
apple	5.0–6.5
potato	4.5–6.0
blackcurrant	6.0–8.0
mint	7.0–8.0
onion	6.0–7.0
strawberry	5.0–7.0
lettuce	6.0–7.0

pH all around you

▶ In your group discuss the following pictures

- Decide whether you all agree with the statements.
- Choose one statement to test. What would you do?
- If there is time, your teacher may let you try this.

You can use lemon juice to remove 'scale' from a kettle.

If we measure the pH of rainwater, it can tell us about air pollution.

All shampoos are pH balanced.

Acid drop sweets are not really acids.

acid

Vinegar is an acid. It should carry a hazard warning.

---

1 Make a drawing to show which plant would grow best in each pot.

2 Lime has a pH value of about 9.
Citric acid has a pH value of about 4.
Which should you add to a neutral soil to grow apples?

3 Acids and alkalis can be dangerous substances.
You must be careful when you use them.
Design a warning poster for your laboratory.

4 Plan an investigation to see how the pH of soil depends on the amount of lime added to it.

5 Fertilisers are used to help plants grow.
They give nutrients (food) to the soil and can change its pH value.
Do you think we should use fertilisers?
Why? Why not?

Things to do

Questions

1 Design and make a poster to explain the word *acid*.
Use key words and clear drawings.

2 Indicators can be made by crushing some plants and vegetables with a liquid. You can use propanone or methylated spirit to make an indicator with red cabbage.
Jill says that propanone is better at removing the colour.
Plan an investigation to see if she is right.

3 Write a report on the different uses of acids in the home.

4 Make a list of all the chemical indicators you have used in this topic.
Which indicator was the most useful? Why?

5 Read the letter to a newspaper shown here. Write a reply to Mr. Clark. Say whether you agree or disagree with his ideas.

I'm fed up with all these chemical tankers on our roads. Many of them carry dangerous things such as acids. Any spills from the tankers could kill people. I think tankers should only be allowed to use the roads between 11 pm and 6 am. Then there are fewer cars around. I want the government to make this law. Will others support me?
Mr. C. Clark

6 A local farmer wants to neutralise his acidic soil. He cannot decide whether to use CALCOLIME or SUPERCAL for this.
a) Plan an investigation to find out which is better at neutralising the soil.
b) What other factors should the farmer consider before choosing which to use?

7 If you leave a half-eaten apple in the air it goes brown.
Keeping pieces of apple in a solution of lemon juice slows down the rate of browning.
Do you think this could be something to do with the pH of the solution?
Plan an investigation to find out if this is the case.

Staying alive

12

How long could you live without oxygen? Not long.
Your lungs take oxygen out of the air.
In your lungs the oxygen passes into your blood.
Your heart pumps the blood all round your body.
No wonder your heart and lungs are so important!

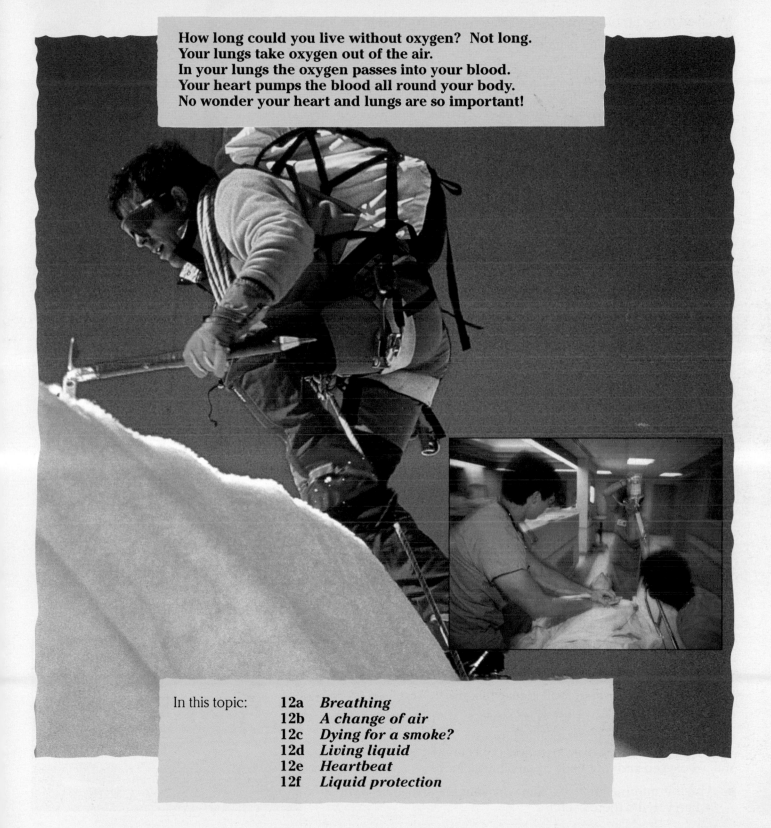

12a Breathing

We all exercise at some time. What exercise have you had in the last week?

Do you feel different after exercise?

▶ Write down some of the changes that happen to your body when you exercise.

Puffing and panting

1 Sit still and count how many times you breathe out in 1 minute.
This is your rate of breathing at rest.

2 Fasten a breathing sensor around your chest.
This will not only measure your **breathing rate** but will also give
you an idea of how **deep** each breath is.

3 Start logging your breathing movements.

4 Copy this table and fill in your breathing rate at rest (you can work
this out by counting the number of peaks on the graph).

Breathing rate at rest (breaths per minute)	Breathing rate after light exercise (breaths per minute)	Breathing rate after heavy exercise (breaths per minute)

5 Now do step-ups for 1 minute (light exercise).
As soon as you have finished, sit down and measure your
breathing rate.
Put your reading in the table.

6 Now do step-ups as quickly as you can for 3 minutes (heavy exercise).
As soon as you have finished, sit down and measure your breathing rate.
Put your reading in the table.

7 Look at the bar-chart data for your breathing rates.

a What happened to   i) your breathing rate in the investigation?
ii) the size of each breath in the investigation?
b Why do you think this happened?
c What do you think affects your breathing rate and your depth of breathing?

Why do we have to breathe?

All the cells in your body need energy to stay alive.
Can you remember where you get your energy?

You get energy out of your food in respiration:

SUGAR + OXYGEN → CARBON DIOXIDE + WATER + ENERGY

Oxygen is needed for respiration to happen.
When sugar is burnt in oxygen, it gives out energy for your cells to use.
You get oxygen into your body by breathing it in.

▶ Use this information to explain why your breathing rate went up
when you did more exercise.

How do you get oxygen into your body?

When you breathe in, air goes down your wind-pipe to your lungs.
Each lung is about the size of a rugby ball.

d Where do you think your lungs are found?

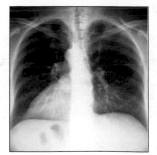
A chest X-ray

Look at the 2 diagrams.
The one at the top shows what the inside of your chest looks like.
The one at the bottom shows a chest model.

e Which part of the human chest is shown by the i) balloons?
ii) bell-jar? iii) rubber sheet? iv) glass tube?

f When you breathe in, do your lungs get bigger (inflate) or
smaller (deflate)?

g What happens to your lungs when you breathe out?

▶ Get the chest model.
Pull the rubber sheet down and then push it up.
Do this a few more times and watch what happens to the balloons.

h When you breathe in, does your **diaphragm** move up or down?

i What happens to it when you breathe out?

▶ Measure the size of your chest with a tape.
Now take in a deep breath.

j What happens to the size of your chest when you breathe in?

k What happens when you breathe out?

▶ Put your hands on your chest.
Breathe in and out deeply and slowly.

l Which way do your ribs move when you breathe in and out?

Muscles raise and lower your ribs and raise and lower your diaphragm.

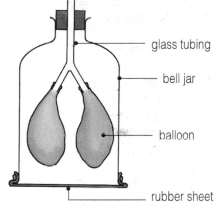
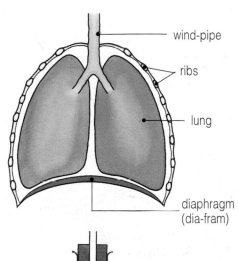

1 Copy and complete the table using the information on this page.

	Breathing in	Breathing out
What do the ribs do? What does the diaphragm do? What happens to the space inside your chest? What happens to your lungs?		

2 Try making your own 'model lungs'.
You could use an old plastic lemonade
bottle, balloons, a rubber-band and a plastic
drinking straw.
Make a hole in the top for the straw and
make it air-tight with plasticine. Cut away
the bottom of the bottle and stretch a
balloon over it for a diaphragm.

3 At the top of high mountains there is far
less oxygen in the air.
a) How do mountaineers manage to
breathe?
b) Why do you think many athletes train at
high altitude?

12b A change of air

"You breathe in oxygen and breathe out carbon dioxide" said Robert.
Do you think that he is right?

▶ Try breathing out through a straw into a test-tube of lime water.
What change did you see?
This is a test for carbon dioxide.

▶ Look at the pie-charts:

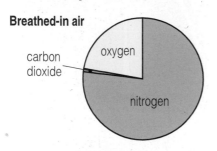

Breathed-in air

carbon dioxide · oxygen · nitrogen

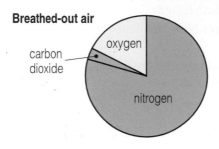

Breathed-out air

carbon dioxide · oxygen · nitrogen

eye protection

a Which gas makes up most of the air you breathe in?

b Which gas do you breathe in more of?

c Which gas do you breathe out more of?

▶ See what happens to a candle when it is left to burn in
i) fresh air and ii) breathed-out air (your teacher will show you
how to collect this).
(Hint: a stop-watch might be helpful.)

d What did you observe?

e Try to explain what you saw.

In and out ...

Set up the apparatus as shown in the diagram:

Breathe gently in and out of the mouth-piece several times.

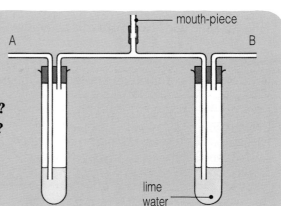

mouth-piece

A   B

lime water

f When you breathe in, does the air come in through A or through B?

g When you breathe out, does the air go out through A or through B?

h In which tube did the lime water turn cloudy first?

Write down your conclusions for your experiment.

Gail said "You must have the same volume of lime water in each tube".
Can you explain why she is right?

Look back at what Robert said at the top of the page.
Can you write out a better sentence?

Looking into your lungs

The diagram shows you how air gets to your lungs through your
wind-pipe and then through the air passages.
The air passages end in tiny bags called **air sacs**. These have very
thin walls. They are surrounded by lots of tiny **blood vessels**.

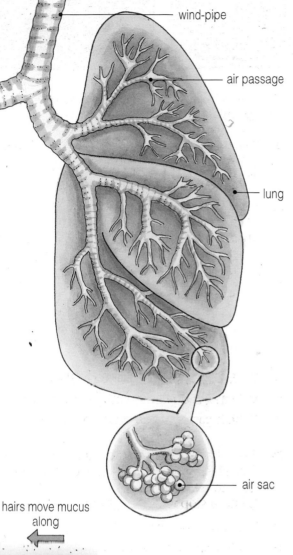

i How do you think oxygen gets from your lungs to all the cells of
your body**?**

j How do you think carbon dioxide gets from the cells of your
body to your lungs**?**

k Which gas do you think passes from the air sacs into the blood
vessels**?**

l Which gas do you think passes in the opposite direction**?**

m These gases are swopped very quickly.
Write down 2 things that help this to happen (hint: read the
sentences above again).

A lot of hot air

▶ Try breathing out onto a cold glass surface, like a beaker of cold
water or a window.
What do you see**?**
Now put a strip of blue **cobalt chloride paper** onto the glass.
What happens**?**
Write down your conclusions.

Can you think of any other differences between the air you breathe
in and the air you breathe out**?**
For one thing, the air you breathe out is *cleaner*.
Your air passages are lined with a slimy liquid called **mucus**.
This traps dust and germs.
Then millions of microscopic **hairs** carry the mucus up to your
nose and throat.

hairs move mucus
along

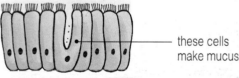

these cells
make mucus

---

1 Copy and complete:
We breathe in air containing nitrogen, ...
and some carbon dioxide. The air that we
breathe . . . . contains the same amount of
. . . ., less . . . . and . . . . carbon dioxide. The
air we breathe out also contains more . . . .
vapour and is at a . . . . temperature.

2 Do you know about **artificial
respiration**?
It's a way of starting up someone's breathing
again.
You can learn about it at a first-aid class.
Your teacher can give you a Help Sheet
explaining how it works.

3 What is mucus?
How does it help to clean up the air that you
breathe in?

4 When you breathe in you take fresh air
into your lungs.
a) Write down the pathway taken by
oxygen from the air outside until it
enters your blood.
b) What happens to the volume of air you
breathe in when you exercise?

Things to do

12c Dying for a smoke?

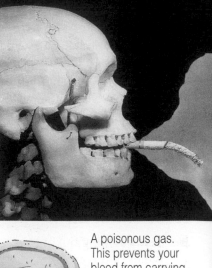

Do you know anyone who smokes?
There are fewer smokers around these days.
Lots of people used to smoke but nowadays they are finding it less attractive.

▶ Write down your ideas about why this is.

Did you know that cigarette smoke is made up of lots of chemicals and many of these are poisonous?
If you smoke, these chemicals go into your body through your mouth and along your air passages.

Fancy this lot?

NICOTINE R.I.P.
An addictive drug. It goes into your blood in the lungs. It causes your blood pressure to rise and your heart to beat faster.

TAR
A brown, sticky substance that collects in your lungs if you breathe in tobacco smoke. It is known to contain substances that cause cancer.

CARBON MONOXIDE R.I.P.
A poisonous gas. This prevents your blood from carrying as much oxygen as it should and so you get out of breath easily.

The smoking machine

First set up the apparatus without the cigarette.

Turn on the suction pump.

After 5 minutes, record:

- the temperature
- the colour of the glass wool
- the colour of the lime water.

Now repeat the experiment with a cigarette.

Record your observations.

What does this experiment tell you about the difference between breathing in fresh air and cigarette smoke?

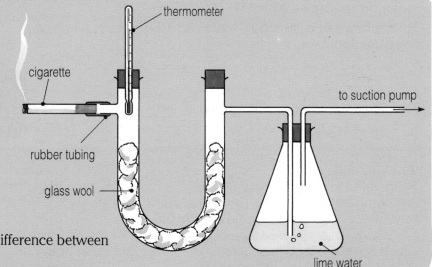

thermometer
cigarette
to suction pump
rubber tubing
glass wool
lime water

Smoking changes people

teeth, fingers and nails turn yellow – that's the nicotine

smoker's cough – to get rid of the mucus

hair and clothes smell – that's the smoke

tongue turns yellow – you can't taste food properly

A mug's game

▶ Read what some people say about smoking.
Design a leaflet for primary school children to explain why they should not start smoking.

Ninety per cent of lung cancer occurs in smokers.

The money spent on cigarettes can't be spent on food, clothes etc.

Smoking increases the risk of serious diseases like bronchitis.

Smokers are 2 to 3 times more likely to die of a heart attack.

You can't keep the smoke to yourself. Everyone around you has to breathe it in.

Illnesses caused by smoking have to be treated. If people did not smoke, this would cost the country less money.

Smoking makes you breathless and less good at sport.

So why start?

Amy is 13. She smokes about 5 cigarettes a day.

▶ Read what Amy has to say about smoking:

"I had my first cigarette when I was 10.
My friend Sharon, she's 2 years older than me, offered me one.
I didn't like it much at first, but it felt exciting somehow.
My Mum would have killed me if she'd found out.
She's always trying to get my Dad to give up but he can't.
I suppose I spend about £4 or £5 a week on cigarettes.
I'll give it up when I'm older because it affects your health.
I'd definitely give up if I ever got pregnant."

In your groups, discuss the reasons why you think people start to smoke.

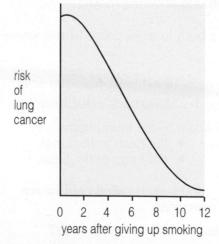

1 Copy and complete:
Cigarette smoke contains poisonous . . . .
One is a drug called . . . . This gets into your blood in the . . . . It causes your blood . . . . to rise and your heart to beat . . . . Tar contains chemicals that cause . . . . A poisonous gas called . . . . stops your blood from carrying as much . . . . as it should.

2 You are asked to talk to some junior school children about the dangers of smoking.
Plan out what you are going to tell them.

3 Write down what you think about the following:
a) Smoking should be banned in shops, offices and on public transport.
b) Once you start smoking it's hard to stop.
c) Smoking costs us all a lot of money.

4 The graph shows how the risk of getting lung cancer changes after giving up smoking.
Explain why you think smokers should give up the habit.

risk of lung cancer

0 2 4 6 8 10 12
years after giving up smoking

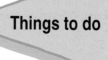

Things to do

143

12d Living liquid

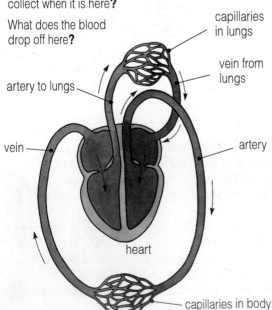

What does blood make you think of?
Horror movies, vampires, wars?

You probably have about 4 litres of blood in your body.
That's a bucket-full.
It's flowing around your body all the time.
But what is it for?

▶ Write down your ideas about how your blood helps you.

You already know that the cells of your body need food and oxygen
to give you energy in respiration.
Your cells make waste chemicals too.
Your kidneys get rid of most of these waste chemicals.

▶ Look at the diagram and answer the questions:

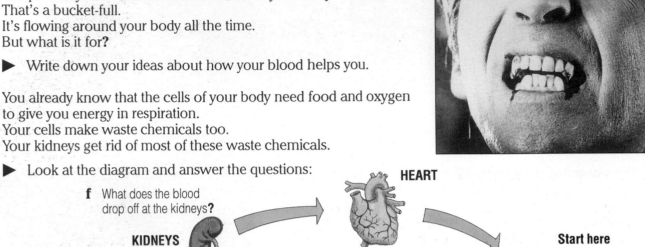

HEART

f What does the blood
drop off at the kidneys?

KIDNEYS

g What keeps
the blood
moving round
and round?

Start here
a What does the blood
collect when it is here?

INTESTINES

e What does the blood take
away from the cells?

d Name 2 things that the blood
drops off that the cells use to live.

**CELLS IN
THE BODY**

LUNGS

b What does the blood
collect when it is here?

c What does the blood
drop off here?

Return journey

So your blood carries many things around your body.
It is rather like a railway system, where trains pick things
up at one place and deliver them to another.

h How do you think the blood is kept on the move?

The blood is carried around your body in tubes called **blood vessels**.

▶ Look at the diagram:

i What do we call tubes that carry blood away from the heart?

j What do we call tubes that carry blood back to the heart?

With your finger, trace the path taken by the blood from:
• the heart to the body
• the body to the heart
• the heart to the lungs
• the lungs to the heart.

Near to the cells are the tiniest blood vessels called **capillaries**.
These connect your arteries to your veins.

k Why do you think that capillaries have very thin walls?

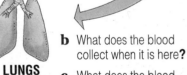

capillaries
in lungs

vein from
lungs

artery to lungs

vein

artery

heart

capillaries in body

Around and around . . .

Do you know how to take your pulse?
When you take your pulse you feel an artery.
Blood flows through your arteries in spurts.
This is the pulse that you feel.

Does your pulse rate and breathing rate go up and down together?

Plan an investigation to see how your pulse and breathing are affected by exercise.

- What exercise will you plan to do?
- What measurements will you take?
- How will you make it a fair test?
- How do you plan to show your results?
- Check your plan with your teacher before carrying it out.

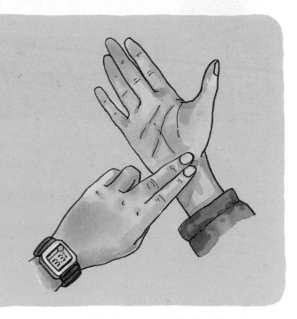

Supply lines

▶ Lift one arm above your head and let the other arm hang at your side. Keep them there for a minute or two.
Now bring them in front of you and look at the differences between the veins on the back of each hand.
What differences can you see?

▶ Look at the photograph of a section of an artery and a vein.

l What differences can you see?

m Can you find out any other differences between arteries and veins?

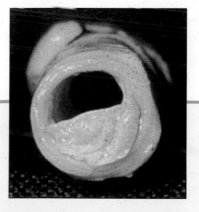

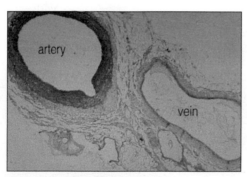

Section of an artery and a vein

Things to do

1 Copy and complete:
Blood is pumped around my body by my
. . . . Blood travels away from my heart in
. . . . and back to my heart in . . . . The tiniest
blood vessels are called . . . . and these have
very . . . . walls so things can pass in and out.
When I feel my pulse I am touching an . . . .

2 Make a table of the differences between arteries and veins. Your teacher can give you a Help Sheet.

3 Sometimes our arteries can get 'furred up'. This is because a fatty substance sticks to the inside of the artery and makes it narrower. How do you think this would affect the flow of blood in the artery?

12e Heartbeat

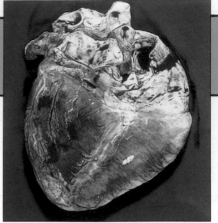

A human heart

What do you think is the strongest muscle in your body?
Not many people think that it is their heart.
Just think of the job your heart does.
It beats about 70 times a minute, for 60 minutes per hour and 24 hours a day, to keep you alive.

a Use a calculator to work out how many times your heart beats:
i) per hour   ii) per day   iii) in a year.

The double pump

Where do you think your heart is?
Put your hand on the place where you think it is.
What can you feel?

b How do you think your heart is protected?

c How many spaces are there inside your heart?

▶ Look at the diagram. It is drawn as though you are facing someone.

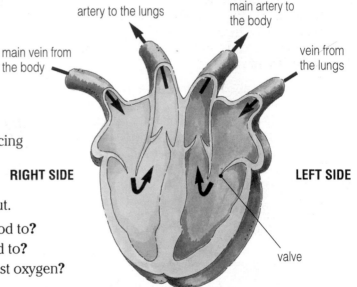

artery to the lungs

main artery to the body

main vein from the body

vein from the lungs

RIGHT SIDE

LEFT SIDE

valve

Your heart is really 2 separate pumps side-by-side.
When your heart beats, the muscle squeezes the blood out.

d Where does the right-side of your heart pump the blood to?

e Where does the left-side of your heart pump the blood to?

f Which side of the heart will have blood containing most oxygen?

Heart listening

The 2 pumps both beat at the same time.
You can hear your partner's heartbeat by using a **stethoscope**.
Try making a home-made version as shown in the diagram.
What sounds can you hear?

You should hear 2 sounds.
Doctors call them lub-dub sounds.
The 2 noises are caused by the **valves** in your heart closing.
Try listening again . . . lub-dub . . . lub-dub . . . lub-dub . . .

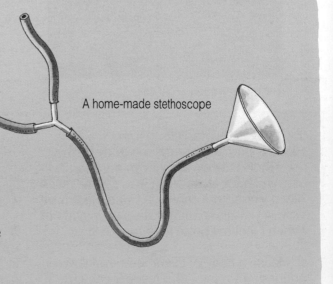

A home-made stethoscope

g Why do you think your heart valves close?
(Hint: look at the top diagram.)

Find out if your heartbeat (the number of beats per minute) is the same as your pulse rate.

h Does it change in the same way as your pulse rate when you exercise?

The big killer

Heart disease is one of the biggest killers in Britain.
Fatty substances can 'fur up' the arteries leading to the heart muscle.

i What would 'furring up' do to the flow of blood to the heart muscle?

j What could happen to the supply of oxygen to the heart muscle?

If the heart muscle does not get enough oxygen it can cause chest pains.
This is called **angina**.
It is a warning that the person is more likely to have a heart attack.

Sometimes a clot can form inside a **coronary artery**.

k How do you think this could cause a **coronary heart attack?**

▶ Look at the cartoons:
In your groups discuss the things that you think can increase the risk of heart attack.
How do you think each of these risks could be reduced?
Make a list of your ideas.

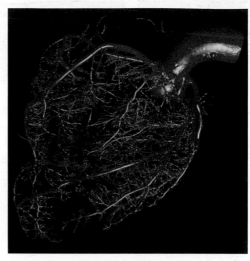

A cast of the coronary arteries

1 Copy and complete:
The heart is made out of .... The blood on the left-side contains .... oxygen than the blood on the .... -side. This is because the blood has just come back from the .... The left-side of the heart pumps blood all around the .... The heart has .... to stop the blood from flowing backwards.

2 Look at the heart diagram opposite. List what happens to the blood as it passes from the main vein to the heart and eventually to the main artery.

3 What sort of person do you think is most likely to suffer a heart attack? How old will they be? What is their weight like? What sort of habits might they have? Draw a cartoon of the person and label it.

4 Design a leaflet or make a poster to let people know about the risks of heart disease.

Things to do

12f *Liquid protection*

Do you know what a **blood transfusion** is?
It once saved Richard's life.
He was involved in a motorway accident.
He was losing a lot of blood.
Fortunately for him, the ambulance team
were quick to arrive.
So they were able to give him extra blood.
But not all our blood is the same.
Richard carried a card that showed which
type his blood was.

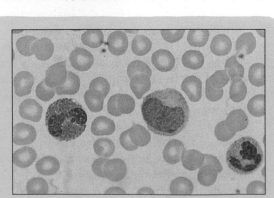

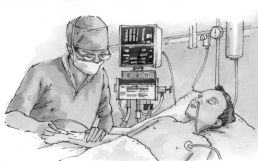

a   There are 4 main blood types. Do you know what they are called?

Each blood type contains slightly different chemicals.

b   Why do you think that you can only have a transfusion of blood
of the same type?

Richard was very grateful to the blood donors who gave their blood.

c   What do you have to do to be a blood donor?

Blood bank

Blood taken from a donor is treated so that it does not clot.
It may settle out into 2 parts. A pale yellow liquid called **plasma**
and a deep red layer of **blood cells**.

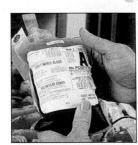

d   Is the blood made up mainly of plasma or blood cells?

Plasma is mainly water containing dissolved chemicals.

Your teacher will give you a prepared slide of blood cells.
Look at it under your microscope.
You will need to focus carefully at high power.

e   Which do you think are bigger: red cells or white cells?

f   Are there more red cells or white cells?

Draw a diagram of each different blood cell that you can see.

g   Can you see any other differences between red and white cells?

h   Why do you think the white cells look purple?

The oxygen carriers

The red cells carry oxygen.
They are red because they contain **haemoglobin**.
This is a chemical that can collect and carry oxygen.
Haemoglobin lets go of oxygen when it comes to a part of the body
that needs it.

i   Where do you think haemoglobin collects oxygen from?

▶   Copy this diagram. Add as many labels and notes to it as you
can to explain how oxygen is carried round your body.

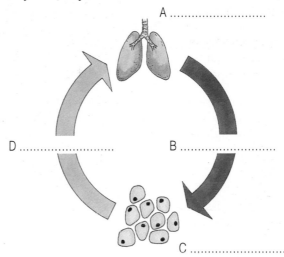

A ....

D ....   B ....

C ....

The protection gang

White cells protect your body from germs.

j   In what ways could germs get into your body?

One sort of white cell *eats* any germs that it finds.
Another sort makes chemicals (called **antibodies**)
that can kill germs.

k   Can you see 2 types of white cell in the photograph at the
bottom of the previous page?
In what ways do they look different?

l   What happens just after you cut yourself?

Eventually a scab will form.
But first the bleeding has to be stopped.
The cut is sealed by lots of tiny bits of cells called **platelets**.

m   Why is it important that the cut is sealed quickly?

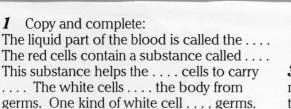

1   Copy and complete:
The liquid part of the blood is called the . . . .
The red cells contain a substance called . . . .
This substance helps the . . . . cells to carry
. . . . The white cells . . . . the body from
germs. One kind of white cell . . . . germs.
Another type makes . . . . that kill germs.

2   Make a table of the differences between
red and white blood cells.

3   People who live at high altitude have far
more red cells than you. Why do you think
this is?

4   These days in science lessons you are
not allowed to take blood samples. Why do
you think this is?

Things to do

Questions

1 Gemma and Beth measured their breathing rate (in breaths per minute) before they ran a race. Then they measured their breathing rates again after the race, every minute, until their rates returned to normal. They recorded their results in a table:

	Before exercise	Minutes after exercise						
		1	2	3	4	5	6	7
Gemma	16	45	38	31	24	20	17	16
Beth	13	35	32	28	22	18	13	13

a) Plot 2 line-graphs on the same sheet. Use the vertical axis for breathing rate and the horizontal axis for time.
b) Who took the longer time to recover from the exercise?
c) Who do you think was the fitter of the two girls? Give your reasons.

2 Where in your body are the following found:
a) diaphragm?   b) air sacs?   c) valves?   d) capillaries?
What job does each one do?

3 Do you think the following statements are true or false?
a) Most of the air you breathe is not used by your body.
b) Smoking does not increase the risk of heart disease.
c) You can get lung cancer by breathing in other people's cigarette smoke.
d) Exercise increases the risk of heart disease.

4 Blood has many different jobs.
Which part of your blood:
a) carries oxygen?   b) carries dissolved food?
c) fights germs?   d) helps your blood to clot?

5 Coronary heart disease can be caused by eating too much saturated fat in foods like meat, butter and cream. You should choose unsaturated fats, in foods like fish and vegetable oils.
Look at food packets and make a list of foods for each of these 2 types of fat.

6 a) Find out where your red blood cells are made.
b) Find out how lack of iron causes **anaemia** and how this affects the body.
c) Why do you think that women take more iron tablets than men?

7 Look at this blood transfusion certificate:
Which blood group does this person belong to?
Make a leaflet or a poster that will persuade people to give blood.

Structure of the Earth

13

The air we breathe is a mixture of gases.

The ground we walk on is made up of 3 types of rock.

The study of these rocks tells us a lot about the history of the Earth.

Rocks don't last forever but are weathered and eroded. Soil forms from particles of rock.

In this topic you will learn about the composition of the air and important uses of the gases it contains. You will also learn about how rocks are formed and re-formed in a constant cycle of change.

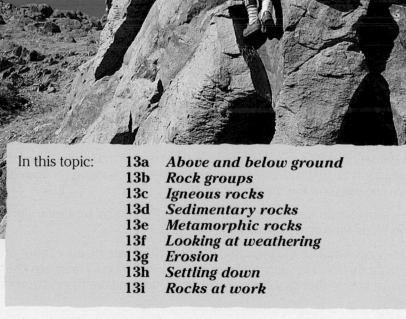

Above and below ground

We live at the bottom of a sea of air called the **atmosphere** that rises for miles above our heads. The composition of air has been known for many years. Air is not a single gas but a mixture of different gases.

The amount of water vapour in the air can vary greatly so the values given for its composition are usually for dry air.

Gas	Typical percentage by volume found in dry air
nitrogen	78.1
oxygen	21.0
argon	0.9
carbon dioxide	0.04

The air around an industrial area, or where there are lots of cars and lorries moving about, may also contain pollutant gases. These could be carbon monoxide, nitrogen oxides and sulphur dioxide.

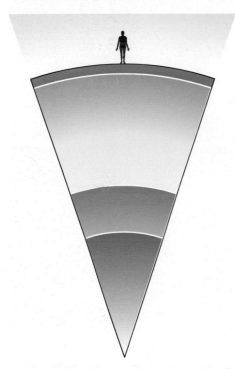

Our knowledge of the structure of the Earth does not come from direct observation. Scientists have been able to build up a picture of what the Earth is like by studying evidence. They can see what happens to the seismic waves caused by earthquakes as they pass through the Earth.

The Earth is divided into 3 main parts.

The **crust** is a thin shell that covers the Earth. The continental crust is above the sea and the ocean crust beneath it. The crust is where we live and grow our food. We obtain all our resources, metals, minerals and fuels from the crust.

Below the crust is a much thicker layer called the **mantle**. This layer is mostly solid but the part near the boundary with the crust is liquid.

At the very centre of the Earth is the **core**. Scientists think that the inner core is solid nickel-iron while the outer core is composed of molten iron together with other elements like sulphur and silicon. The temperature at the core is 4000–4500 °C.

Air is a valuable raw material. All of the gases in air have important uses.

Nitrogen is an unreactive, or inert, gas. It is often used to keep out more reactive gases, like oxygen, from processes.

Like all living things, the micro-organisms that cause food to decay need oxygen to live. Packaging food in an atmosphere of nitrogen helps to prevent the growth of these micro-organisms so the food has a longer shelf-life.

Nitrogen provides an inert atmosphere for many chemical processes including the production of silicon chips for microelectronics.

Nitrogen is essential for the growth of plants. However, plants cannot absorb nitrogen directly from the air. First, it must be made into fertilisers. These are chemicals like ammonium nitrate that dissolve in water in the soil and are then absorbed by the plant roots.

Oxygen is essential for two important processes: respiration and combustion.

Respiration in the cells of our body provides us with the energy we need to live.

> sugar + oxygen → carbon dioxide + water + energy

In our lungs oxygen passes from the air into our blood and carbon dioxide passes out in the opposite direction.

During **combustion** fuels burn in oxygen to release heat energy and waste gases like water and carbon dioxide.

> fuel + oxygen → heat energy + waste gases

In some ways air acts like dilute oxygen.

Fuels burn far more vigorously in pure oxygen than they do in air.

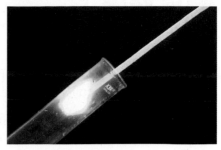

A glowing spill relights in oxygen

Carbon dioxide provides the fizz in fizzy drinks but it has other important uses.

Green plants are able to use energy from the Sun to convert carbon dioxide and water into sugars. A green pigment called **chlorophyll** traps the sunlight. This process is called **photosynthesis**.

> CARBON DIOXIDE + WATER $\xrightarrow[\text{CHLOROPHYLL}]{\text{SUNLIGHT}}$ SUGAR + OXYGEN

Carbon dioxide is used in fire extinguishers. This is because it doesn't let things burn in it and it is denser than air.

Putting out the fire

Put a short candle inside a beaker and add some pieces of calcium carbonate around it.

Light the candle and, while it is burning, carefully put dilute hydrochloric acid onto the calcium carbonate with a teat-pipette.

The chemical reaction between calcium carbonate and dilute hydrochloric acid produces carbon dioxide gas. What happens to the candle?

1 Copy and complete the following:
a) The Earth underground is divided into 3 parts . . . . , ... and . . . .
b) We get all the resources we need from the . . . .
c) The inner . . . . is made from nickel-iron and is . . . .
d) The . . . . is mostly solid but is liquid where it meets the crust.

2 Using the information given in the table opposite, draw a pie-chart to illustrate the composition of dry air.

3 NPK fertilisers contain chemicals that have nitrogen (N) and two other elements. What two other elements are represented by the symbols P and K? Can you find the name of a chemical compound that contains each of these elements?

4 Find out what types of fire extinguisher are available in your school. Can they all be used to tackle any type of fire? For what kind of fire is a dry powder extinguisher and not a foam extinguisher used?

Things to do

13b Rock groups

Rocks are found in many different shapes and sizes.
Maybe you have climbed some of the larger ones ...
or maybe you have collected some.

Rocks can tell us a lot about the history of our planet, Earth.

People who study rocks are called **geologists**.
Let's see how good a geologist you can be!

Testing rocks

Carry out these tests on each rock sample.

Your teacher will give you some Rock Data Cards.
Write down the results for each rock on a new Rock Data Card.

Rock test 1 – What does the rock look like?

Use a magnifying glass to observe the rock carefully.
- What colour is it?
- Is it shiny or dull?
- Is it rough or smooth?
- Can you see any crystals or grains?

Rock test 2 – Is the rock hard?

Try to scratch the rock.
Rocks which can be scratched by a fingernail are called **very soft**.
Rocks which can be scratched by an iron nail are called **soft**.
Rocks which can be scratched by a steel knife are called **hard**.
Rocks which cannot be scratched by a steel knife are called **very hard**.

Rock test 3 – Does the rock break easily?

Wrap the sample in a cloth. Put it on the floor.
Lower your heel onto the rock. Push down.
Does the rock break?

Rock test 4 – Does the rock soak up water?

Put the sample on a watch-glass.
Use a pipette to drop water on to it.
What happens to the water?

Look at your Rock Data Cards. Study the properties of the samples.

Now divide the rocks into groups. List your groups.

Write down the properties you have used to make groups.

Rock data card	
Sample number	
Rock test 1	
Rock test 2	
Rock test 3	
Rock test 4	
Other information	

Rocks contain different particles or grains.
Some grains fit together well.
But in some rocks the grains do not fit so well.

Think about the rocks which soak up water.
Where do you think the water goes?
What does this tell you about how the grains fit together?

Measure how much water a rock soaks up

Another way of grouping rocks is by the way they were made.

There are 3 main types of rock.
The 3 types were formed in different ways.

Granite (igneous)

Igneous rocks
These form when melted ('molten')
substances cool.
These rocks are usually hard.
They are made of crystals.
Granite is an igneous rock.

Sandstone (sedimentary)

Sedimentary rocks
These form in layers. They are made
when substances settle out in water.
Sometimes they contain fossils.
These rocks are usually soft.
Sandstone and **limestone** are
sedimentary rocks.

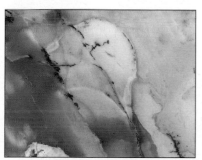

Marble (metamorphic)

Metamorphic rocks
These rocks form much more slowly.
They are made when rocks are heated
and pushed together.
They are usually very hard.
Marble is a metamorphic rock formed
from limestone.

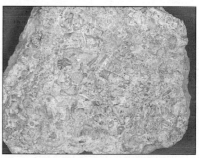

Limestone (sedimentary)

Things to do

1 Copy and complete the following:
a) There are 3 main types of rock: . . . . ,
. . . . and . . . .
b) . . . . rocks form when hot liquids cool
and become solid.
c) . . . . rocks form as substances settle in
layers.
d) . . . . rocks form when other rocks are
heated and pushed together.

2 Use your rock test findings, books and
computer to decide whether your rock
samples were igneous, sedimentary or
metamorphic.

3 Some types of rock are used in buildings.
a) What are the ideal properties of a rock
used for building?
b) Find out what types of rock are used for
your local buildings.
Draw a poster
about this to
display in your
local library.

4 Can you explain
how the rocks in this
photograph have
changed?

Igneous rocks

Igneous rocks are made from **magma**. This is a molten (melted) material from deep underground.
Magma rises to the surface of the Earth. It can erupt at the surface to form a **volcano**.
The molten rock that erupts is called **lava**. It cools *quickly* at the surface to form solid rock. Some magma never reaches the surface. It cools *slowly* surrounded by rocks underground. It forms solid rock.

▶ Volcanoes can be dangerous.
But some people choose to live on the slopes of volcanoes.
Why do they do this?
Make a list of your ideas.

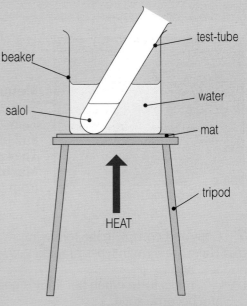

Igneous rocks are made up of crystals.
The crystals may be tiny or quite large.
Why does the size of crystal vary?
Does it depend on how fast the magma cools?
Try the next experiment to find out.

Crystal clues

We can't easily melt rocks in the lab!
Use salol to be your melted rock for this test.

⚠️ Care – the water will still be hot.

- Half fill a beaker with water.

- Put a solid called *salol* into a test-tube.
  It should be about 3 cm deep.

- Put your test-tube into the beaker of water.

- Heat the water to melt the salol.

- When the salol has melted, switch off your Bunsen burner.

- Ask your teacher for a *cold* glass slide.
  This has been kept in the fridge.

- Use a pipette to put 3 drops of melted salol on to the cold slide.
  Use a magnifying glass to watch carefully.
  You will see salol crystals form.

Crystals can form when a liquid cools.

- Now get a *warm* slide. Repeat your experiment.

a On which slide did the salol cool faster?

b On which slide did the bigger crystals form?

c Write a summary of your findings.

Comparing rocks

Your teacher will give you some rock samples.
Look carefully at the rocks.

Make a table to show your answers to the following:

- Describe the appearance of each rock.
- Decide which of the rocks are igneous rocks.

For the igneous rocks:

- How quickly did the magma cool to form each rock?
  How do you know?
- Did the rock form by cooling **above** or **below** ground?

▶ Look at these statements about igneous rocks.
  They describe how the rock forms.
  Put them in the right order. Copy out your answer.

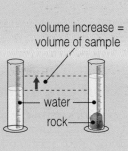

| Inside the Earth is magma. This is very hot molten rock. |
| The volcano erupts. |
| It cools slowly underground. |
| Lava cools quickly. It makes igneous rocks with small crystals. |
| It makes igneous rocks with large crystals. |
| Then magma comes to the surface of the Earth. It is called lava. |
| Some magma does not get to the surface. |

d Igneous rocks do not contain fossils. Why not?

Igneous rocks are hard. They are used to surface roads. They are usually coated with tar.

Density of rocks

Measure the density of the samples of granite and gabbro.
Granite is 'silica-rich'. Gabbro is 'iron-rich'.

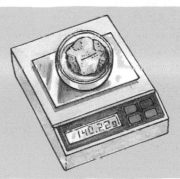

volume increase =
volume of sample

water
rock

e Which of these rocks is the denser?

Now measure the density of the other igneous rocks.
Decide whether the rocks you test are relatively
'silica-rich' or 'iron-rich'.

---

1 Copy and complete:
a) Molten rock is called . . . .
b) Molten rock erupting from a volcano is called . . . .
c) Fast cooling of a liquid makes . . . . crystals.
d) Slow cooling of a liquid makes . . . . crystals.

2 Use books and ICT to help you with this.
a) What is a volcano?
b) Imagine that you are a newspaper reporter. You have been sent to report on an erupting volcano. You are the first at the scene. Write the report for your newspaper.

3 Find out about:
a) volcanoes in the world which are 'active'.
b) a famous volcanic eruption. (How did this affect local people? What happened to the environment?)

Things to do

13d Sedimentary rocks

Are you all OK?

Yes, we're just weathered.

Rocks are slowly weathered. They break into pieces. You will learn more about this process later in the topic.

The weathered rocks are moved by wind, rivers and the sea. They are **transported** to another place. When these settle (**deposit**), they are called **sediments**.
The sediments can be fine grains, like sand. They can be larger fragments, like pebbles.

Over time, layers of sediment build up. The sediment is squeezed by the weight of new layers above. Any water is squeezed out. The minerals dissolved in the water are left behind. These minerals **cement** the grains together. The solid sedimentary rock forms.

When seas or lakes run dry, sediments form. The water evaporates.

Look at the diagram:

a   Which is the newest sediment deposited?

b   Which is the oldest rock?

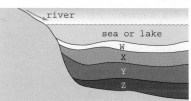

river

sea or lake

W
X
Y
Z

Layers of sedimentary rock forming.

Sand and sandstone

Look closely at the samples of damp sand and sandstone.
Use a hand lens or microscope.
How are the grains held together?

Squash the wet sand. Look for the water being squeezed out.
You can see how the sediments stick together.

Looking at sedimentary rocks

Look carefully at the rock samples your teacher gives you.
These are all sedimentary rocks.
Use books or ROMs to identify them.

Make a list of *features* of sedimentary rocks (appearance, texture, etc.).

c   Name the rock made from pebbles.

d   Name the rock made from mud.

e   Fossils are often found in sedimentary rock. Why?

Testing limestones

Your teacher will show you some samples of limestones.
Are the limestones the same or different?

Plan the tests you will do to answer the questions below.
Be sure you know which measurements to make.

- What do the limestones look like?
- Do they soak up water?
- What are their densities?
- How much carbonate do they contain?

Ask your teacher to check your plans.
Then carry out the tests.
Record your results in a table.

f Are all limestones the same?

g Why do you think this is?

h Are your results reliable? How can you improve these tests?

Fossils are sometimes found in sedimentary rocks. They tell us about the animals and plants that lived millions of years ago.
They are the remains of animals and plants that have been preserved in rocks.

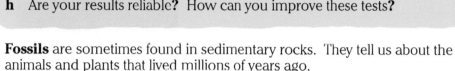

▶ Look at the fossil your group has been given.

How do you think this fossil formed?

Use books or ROMs to find out about your fossil.
- When did it live?
- Where did it live?
- What was its environment like?

Write a paragraph about your fossil.

Draw a picture of your fossil and colour it in.

1 Draw a cartoon strip to show the process of forming a sedimentary rock. Start with a piece of weathered rock. Finish with the solid lump!

2 A river carries rock fragments from a mountain to the sea. Describe 2 ways in which the fragments change as they are moved.

3 Why can the presence of fossils be useful in the investigation of rocks?

4 Imagine that a limestone quarry is opening near you. You are a local newspaper reporter. Write a balanced report about the quarry.
Explain why the quarry is important.
Write about problems that might arise.

Things to do

Metamorphic rocks

Metamorphic rocks can be formed from igneous, sedimentary or other metamorphic rocks.

Some rocks are buried deep underground. They are hot. They feel pressure from rocks above them.
Sometimes the heat and pressure are so great that the mineral structures of the rocks change. The particles in the buried rock form new crystals.
Metamorphic rock is formed.
These changes happen when the rock is still solid. It does not melt.

Sometimes rocks are 'baked' by magma.

a What is magma**?**

The rocks close to the magma get very hot. The high temperature can change the mineral structure of the rock. It becomes **metamorphic** rock.

The minerals in metamorphic rocks line up in bands.

What's changed?

Sedimentary rocks can become new metamorphic ones.
Your teacher will give you some rock samples.
Look at the rocks with a hand lens.
Match the **sedimentary** rock with the **metamorphic** rock it makes.

Choose one matching pair of rocks.
Describe the differences between the rocks.

▶ Look at this rock face diagram:
   It shows 3 types of rock.

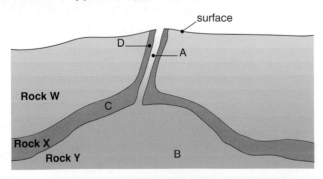

surface

D — A

Rock W   C

Rock X

Rock Y   B

b Which rock is sedimentary**?**

c Which rock is igneous**?**

d Which rock is metamorphic**?**

e The rock at A cooled more quickly than the rock at B.
   How does that affect its appearance**?**

f Why is the band of rock thicker at C than at D**?**

3 rock types!

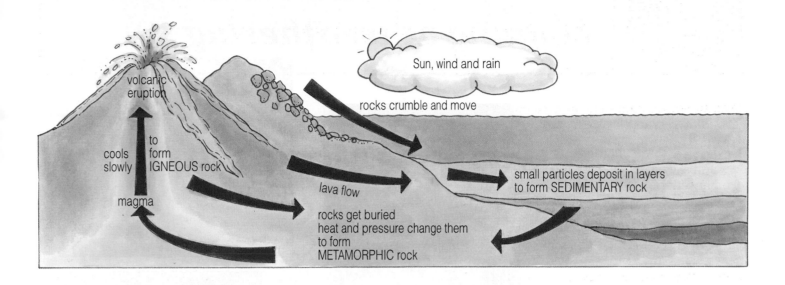

volcanic eruption

Sun, wind and rain

rocks crumble and move

cools slowly — to form IGNEOUS rock

magma

lava flow

small particles deposit in layers to form SEDIMENTARY rock

rocks get buried
heat and pressure change them
to form
METAMORPHIC rock

g   This is called the **rock cycle**. Why do you think this is**?**

Identifying rocks

These could be features to look for:

Igneous	Sedimentary	Metamorphic
Hard	Can be soft and crumbly (but not always!)	Hard
Made of crystals No layers	Made of lots of grains	Made of bands or sheets Splits into layers
No fossils	May contain fossils	May contain distorted fossils

- Use these ideas to sort some rock samples into groups.
- Name as many of the rocks as you can.
- Use books or ROMs to list some uses of these rocks.

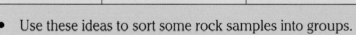

1   Copy out the 2 lists of rocks.
Use a line to join each sedimentary rock with the metamorphic rock it makes.

Sedimentary	Metamorphic
limestone	quartzite
sandstone	marble
shale	slate

2   Fossils found in metamorphic rock are often distorted. Why?

3   You must get permission for this first!
Visit a local garden centre or builder's yard.
Make a list of the rocks you see.
How are the rocks used?

4   Find out some information about *earthquakes*.
a) What causes earthquakes?
b) What is the *epicentre* of an earthquake?
c) What is the *Richter scale*?
d) What is a *seismometer*?
e) Why is San Francisco at risk from earthquakes?

Things to do

Looking at weathering

Rocks don't stay the same forever. They slowly crumble away.

▶ Look at these photographs and say what you think has caused the rocks to change in each case.

The process that makes rocks crumble is called **weathering**. Weathering can be caused by water, wind and changes of temperature.

Acid attack

Do you remember looking at how acid rainwater affected limestone in Topic 11?

Carry out an investigation to see if acid affects other rocks in the same way.

Add a few drops of acid to chalk.

Write down what you see.

⚠ acid

acid

Repeat your investigation with granite, sandstone and marble chips.

Frost damage

Water can get into cracks in rocks.

If the water freezes, it turns to ice. But ice takes up more space than water. So the ice can split the rock into smaller pieces. This is called frost damage.

Your teacher will fill a small glass bottle with water and screw the top on tightly.

The bottle is then put into a strong plastic bag, which is tied and put into a freezer.

In the next lesson your teacher will show you what has happened to the bottle.

This limestone cave was weathered out by water.

Large **stalactites** hang from the roof of the cave.

How do you think they formed**?**

Investigating weathering

Look at rocks around your school for signs of weathering.
You can also look at bricks and other building materials.

- Are the weathered rocks soft**?**
  Scratch them with an iron nail to find out.
- What colour are they**?**
  Is their colour different from that of unchanged rock**?**
- Are there any cracks in their surface**?** What are the cracks like**?**
- What do you think caused the weathering in each case**?**
- What types of rock crumble most easily**?**
- What types of rock last the longest**?**

Look to see how mosses, lichens and other plants can change rocks.
Examine the rock underneath these plants and then carefully
replace them.

▶ Find out about different types of
weathering:
  • physical weathering
  • chemical weathering
  • biological weathering.

---

1 Copy and complete the following:
The process that makes rocks crumble
is called . . . . Soft rocks crumble more
easily than . . . . rocks. Rocks break up
due to the action of . . . . , ... or . . . .
Rain can weather rocks because it is
. . . . When water gets into cracks it
can . . . . to form . . . . which takes up
more space and so it can split the rock
into smaller pieces.

2 Look at this diagram. Write an
explanation of how loose scree
forms.

loose scree

3 Visit your nearest
churchyard or cemetery.
But never go on your own.
Always take a friend or an
adult with you.
Look carefully at the
different types of gravestone.
Some will have weathered
more than others.
What are the earliest dates
that you can read? These
will be on the hardest rocks.
Try to name the different
types of rock and note the
earliest date on each.

Things to do

Erosion

Weathering makes rocks crumble into smaller pieces.

These pieces are then carried away by other things, e.g. wind, and so the rock wears away.

This wearing away of rocks is called **erosion**.

CRUMBLE COTTAGE
LAND-SLIDE WRECKS CLIFF HOMES

The Robinsons are moving house, because their house is on the move.
The garden is not what it was, in fact it's nearly all gone.

The floors are tilting and the walls are cracking.
The Robinsons, who have lived there for 30 years, said 'We are so sad. When we

bought the house we never thought that this would happen.'

▶ Study the newspaper article above and then write down your answers to these questions.

a   Why do you think the Robinsons bought a house so close to the cliff edge?

b   What do you think caused the land-slide?

c   Is there any way it could have been prevented?

d   What do you think has happened to all the bits of rock that have been eroded from the cliff?

▶ Look at these 3 photographs. For each one, write down what you think is causing the erosion of the rocks.

e

f

g

| **Weathering**
The rocks break into pieces. | → | **Erosion**
The small pieces of rock rub against others as they move. They get smaller themselves and they wear away other rocks as they move along. |

The pieces of rock are often found a long way from where they started.
Rock pieces are transported by rivers.

How are rocks eroded by water?

Make a 'stream' flowing into a 'lake'.
Investigate how the stream moves rocks.
Is the movement affected by:

- how fast the stream flows?
- the width of the stream?
- the type of rock?
- the size of rock?

Make a prediction which you could test.

Write a plan to test your prediction.

How can you make your results reliable?

Show your plan to your teacher and then try it out.

Write a report saying what you did and what you found out.

Was your plan a good one?

How could you improve your investigation?

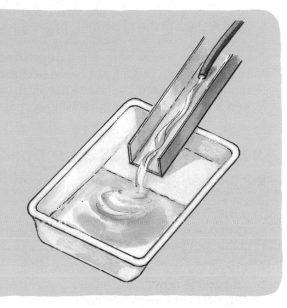

Solve the mystery

▶ Look at these 2 photographs.
Write down your answers to these questions.

h How do you think erosion has formed the **arch** and the **stacks**?

i Where has the material that was eroded ended up?

1 Copy and complete, choosing the correct word from the 2 given in brackets in each case:
Rocks crumble due to (weathering/erosion) and are then worn away by (weathering/erosion). (Winds/waves) break off pieces of rock when they smash against (hills/cliffs). Glaciers are rivers of (ice/water) that scrape rock out of (mountains/valleys). (Larger/smaller) pieces of rock are carried further away than (larger/smaller) pieces.

2 Design a model to show how waves erode cliffs.
What will you make the cliffs out of?
How will you make the waves hit the cliffs?

3 In very dry countries, winds can pick up sand and blow it against large rocks.
Look at this photograph of a **rock pedestal**.
Try to explain how these are formed in the desert.

4 Ask your teacher for some pebbles from a beach. What sort of shapes do they have? How do you think they have become shaped like this?

Things to do

Settling down

After rocks are broken down, the smaller pieces may be carried away. We say that they are **transported** to another place.

▶ In what ways can the pieces be transported to another place? Look back at the previous 2 pages for some ideas.

Eventually the pieces of rock are **deposited** in another area.
Very small pieces of rock are called **sediments**.
Sediments deposited by the sea may form sand banks.
When a river deposits sediments, they may eventually form a soil.

Near a sandy bay

Where does the soil come from?

▶ Your teacher will give you samples of 4 different soils.
These will be labelled A, B, C and D.
Each of these soils has come from a different place.

Look very carefully at each soil using a hand lens.
Try to match each soil with one of the places shown in these photographs.
Write down the reasons for your choice.

Moorland

Farmland

Woodland

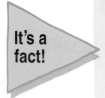

It's a fact!

Sandy soils have large particles and clay soils have small particles. **Loam soils** are a mixture of sandy soil and clay soil. They are easy to dig and hold water without becoming water-logged.
Dead plants and animals decay in soil to form a soft black substance called **humus**.

Investigating soils

Your teacher will give you 2 different soil samples.
You can choose one of these investigations:

A Which soil contains more water?

C Which soil will hold the most water?

B Which soil contains more humus?
(Hint: humus burns off at 110°C.)

D In which soil do seeds grow better?

Plan your investigation. Make sure it is a fair test.

- What equipment will you need?
- How will you record your results?

Looking at sediments

▶ Look very carefully at your rock and soil sample with a hand lens. Are all the particles the same size?

▶ Pour some of your material into a jam jar or measuring cylinder. There should be enough to fill the measuring cylinder to a depth of about 4 cm.

Now almost fill the container with water. Put your hand over the top and carefully shake the container, so that you mix the solid up with the water.

Leave the solid to settle.
Look at it regularly during the lesson

Write down what you can see.

Have another look at it next lesson.

What does this experiment tell you about sediments?

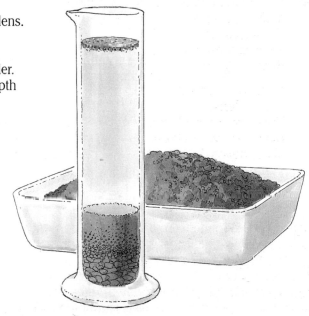

---

1 Copy and complete:
Soils are made of small . . . . particles. These have broken away from large rocks by . . . . and . . . . Then they may have been . . . . by the action of rivers and streams. Sediments are small . . . . particles. Some may have been . . . . by the sea to form sand.

2 Try to explain each of the following statements:
a) Sandy soils are easy to dig but need plenty of rain.
b) Clay soils can get water-logged and are then hard to dig.

3 The rock cycle:

Rocks can be broken down by weathering and erosion. They can then be transported and deposited somewhere else. When they build up as sediments they become squashed together to form a new rock.

Make a poster or patterned note of the rock cycle.

4 Estuaries are places where rivers meet the sea. The sediment carried by the river is deposited as mud. Find out about estuaries and mud-flats.

Things to do

Rocks at work

13i

Limestone

Limestone is a sedimentary rock made from the shells of sea creatures.

It is made of calcium carbonate.

Limestone is a very important rock.
Blocks of it are used to construct buildings.

We also use limestone to make other building materials, such as **cement**. Cement is then mixed with more rock products to make **mortar** and **concrete**.

When we make **cement** the limestone is ground up into a powder and heated with clay. A little calcium sulphate is then added to it.

The mixture is heated in large rotating kilns.
Look at the diagram of the kiln:

When limestone is heated it breaks down into calcium oxide and carbon dioxide gas is given off.

Mortar is made by mixing cement powder with sand, then adding water to make a thick paste.
It is the material that binds the bricks together when a house is built.

Concrete is made from a mixture of cement, sand and gravel or small stones. As with mortar, we then add water and mix it all together.
Reinforced concrete is made when we need large blocks, such as for building motorway bridges. The concrete is set in moulds with iron rods running through them.

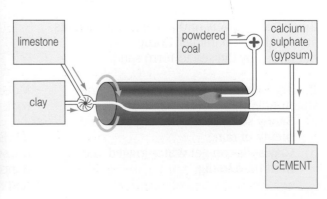

Granite

Granite is a course-grained igneous rock and is usually pink or grey. It is very hard and ideal for constructing buildings that will last for a long time.

It is not damaged by acid rain like limestone.

a Which city is known as the 'granite city'?

Slate

Slate is a fine-grained metamorphic rock. It is often grey or black but may also have a brownish, greenish or bluish appearance.

It can be split into thin layers and it doesn't allow water to pass through so it is ideal for the roof of a building.

▶ Did you know that before pencils and paper became available in schools pupils would write on slates using chalk? When they finished their lesson they would wipe the slate clean so it could be written on again. This is where we get the expression 'to wipe the slate clean' that means to give someone a fresh start.

A snooker table has a slate bed covered in green baize (a woollen fabric). The top of the table must be absolutely flat to allow the balls to move as truly as possible.

---

1 Copy and complete:
a) . . . . is used to make cement.
b) A mixture of cement, sand and water makes . . . . This is used for . . . .
c) A mixture of cement, gravel and water makes . . . . This is used for . . . .

2 Here are 3 rocks we use for building: limestone, granite and slate.
a) Which is an igneous rock? How are igneous rocks formed?
b) Which is a sedimentary rock? How are sedimentary rocks formed?
c) Which is a metamorphic rock? How are metamorphic rocks formed?

3 Carry out a survey of the buildings near to where you live to see what materials have been used to make them. Make a list of the materials. What is the commonest material used?

4 Find out:
a) How rocks like limestone, granite and slate are quarried. (Quarries are dangerous places. You must not go into a quarry without permission.)
b) How manufactured building materials like bricks and concrete blocks are made.

Things to do

Questions

1 Say whether each of the following statements is *true* or *false*.
a) Sedimentary rocks are usually very hard.
b) Igneous rocks form when molten materials cool.
c) Rocks are often found on beaches.
d) Sandstone is a sedimentary rock.
e) There are 2 main types of rock.

2 Draw pictures of some of the rock samples you tested.
Cut out the pictures.
Stick them on to the backs of your Rock Data Cards.

3 Explain how each of these rocks is formed:
a) granite
b) conglomerate
c) slate.

4 Sea defences can be used to limit coastal erosion.
Concrete can be used to build them.
Concrete is made from sand, cement and gravel mixed with water.
Plan an investigation to test different concrete mixes.
Which will make the best sea defence?
(You must be able to do your tests in the lab.)

5 Look at the simple rock cycle:
Choose words from the list below to put labels in the boxes.

heat   melting   erosion   deposition   pressure
weathering   transportation   crystallising

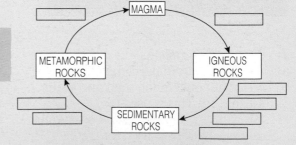

MAGMA

METAMORPHIC ROCKS

IGNEOUS ROCKS

SEDIMENTARY ROCKS

6 Find out about geological time periods.
During your research, try to answer the questions below.
a) In which period were there lots of sea animals, but no life on land?
b) In which period did the Ice Age occur?
c) Which period lasted from about 135 million to 65 million years ago?
d) In which period did reptiles start to appear on Earth?
e) Which geological time period are we in today?

In the cretaceous period, great reptiles roamed the Earth.

Environment

14

What is your environment?

It includes your house, your school, your street – in fact, all of your surroundings.

Animals and plants are affected by their environment.

This topic is about how living things depend upon their environment for their survival.

sparrowhawk

caterpillar

butterfly

oak leaves

squirrel

jay

robin

badger

acorn

mushrooms

grass snake

stoat

lichen

grass

primrose

frog

fly

toad

slug

foxglove

blackberries

A place to live

The place in which a plant or animal lives is called its **habitat**. The **habitat** must provide everything that the living thing needs to survive.

▶ Your house is part of your habitat. What does it provide for you?

▶ Make a list of some things that animals need to survive. Make a list of some things that plants need to survive.

▶ Look at the photographs and write down how each living thing is able to survive in its own habitat.

Cactus plants live in dry habitats. Their leaves are sharp spines. They store water inside their thick stems.

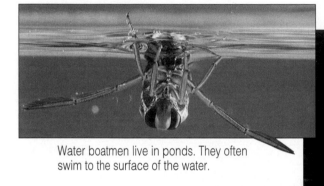

Water boatmen live in ponds. They often swim to the surface of the water.

Many woodland birds build their nests in holes in trees.

Angler fish live in the deep sea. No plants live there as it is always dark.

How do small animals survive?

Small animals live in habitats around your school. Because they live there successfully we say that they are **adapted** to the habitat. They will not be easy to see. Many small creatures hide in long grass, under leaves and in cracks in bark or rocks. Many come out only at night. Here are some ways of finding animals. Choose the one that best suits the habitat.

Pooters

These are small containers with two tubes attached. You suck in through one tube and point the other at the small animal you want to collect. The gauze makes sure you don't get a mouthful of insect. Make sure you suck through the right tube!

My goodness! It's windy today!

Sweep nets

Many insects hide in long grass. A strong net is swept through the grass about 10 times so that the insects drop off into the net bag. You can use a pooter to collect them from the bag.

Uh-uh!

Tree beating

Trees and bushes provide food for many small animals. You can collect them by placing a white sheet under a branch. Shake or bang the branch with a stick so that the animals fall out. Take care not to damage the branch. Collect the animals with a pooter.

Help!

Pitfall traps

You can set yoghurt pots into holes in the ground. The rim of the pot must be level with the soil surface.

Look at the picture. How do you think small animals get trapped?

Don't sink the rim below soil level or water may enter. Pitfall traps should be left overnight.

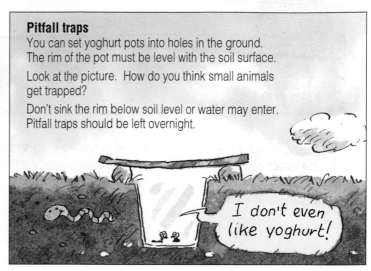

I don't even like yoghurt!

▶ Use a hand lens to study the animals that you have collected.

Be very careful not to damage them.

Your teacher will give you a sheet to help you find out their names.

▶ Where exactly are they found? Do they live on particular food plants? Are they well camouflaged? If so why?

What conditions do they like to live in?

Do they prefer light or dark? Dry or damp?

▶ Record your findings in a table like this:

Name of animal	Number in sample	How is it adapted to living in its habitat?
Centipede	2	Moves very fast on many legs. Has large jaws.

Return all animals, unharmed, to where you found them.

Things to do

1 Match up the following living things with their correct habitats:

moss	pond
trout	hedge
squirrel	path
frog	stream
dandelion	wall
hawthorn	wood

2 List some conditions that make life difficult in the following habitats:
a) stream   c) seashore rock-pool
b) hedge   d) mountain.

3 Explorers have been able to survive in very bad conditions. How have they stayed alive:
a) in outer space?
b) at the bottom of the sea?
c) in the frozen Arctic?

4 Write a letter to your pen friend on the planet Zorgan. Explain what conditions are like on Earth. Talk about your own habitat and the animals and plants that share it with you.

Changing seasons

A

B

C

D

We notice the weather getting colder in the winter and we put on warmer clothes. But how do animals and plants survive the changes?

▶ Look at these 4 photographs. Discuss with the others in your group which photograph was taken in which season. Give reasons for your choice.

Plants in winter

A garden in winter looks very bare compared with in summer. Many plants seem to have disappeared. Many of those that you can see have lost all their leaves. Why do you think this is?

Many plants survive the winter as seeds in the ground. What happens to these in the next spring or summer?

▶ Look at this picture of a daffodil. How do you think it is able to stay alive below the ground in winter?

Many trees lose their leaves in order to survive in winter. They grow new leaves in the spring.

▶ List 3 trees that lose their leaves in winter. List 3 trees or shrubs that keep their leaves all year round. Look at some of these leaves. Write down your ideas about why they're good leaves for winter.

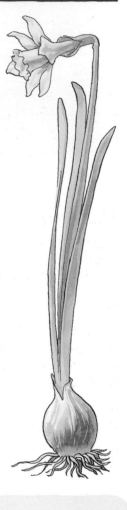

Shivering seeds!

Gardeners usually sow pea seeds at the end of the spring. They do this so that the young pea plants are not killed by frost. The plants grow and the new peas can be picked in the summer.

Some new varieties of pea seeds are able to survive frost. This means that they can be sown earlier in the year. Why would this be useful to the gardener?

Plan an investigation to find out how well seeds survive frost.

Remember that you must make it a fair test.

What other conditions might affect the growth of the seeds?

How long will your investigation take?

Think how you are going to record your results.

Show your plan to your teacher.

Then start your investigation.

Hibernation

Do you know where all the greenfly go in winter? They lay eggs with a very tough coat to help them to survive the cold. The old greenfly then die and the new greenfly hatch out in the spring.

Ladybirds feed on greenfly, but in the winter they have no food. So ladybirds **hibernate** in cracks in bark and under dead leaves.

Many small animals like hedgehogs, squirrels, dormice and frogs hibernate. They eat a lot towards the end of the summer and build up a layer of fat under their skin. Then they find a quiet spot and go to sleep for the winter.

▶ Write down your answers to these questions.

a Give some reasons why animals hibernate.

b How are they able to go without food for so long?

c What do you think will happen to the fat layer during the winter?

Migration

Have you seen birds flying off in the autumn? Swallows and martins escape the winter by flying to warmer countries. This is called **migration**.

▶ List some of the problems that birds face in winter.

Some birds visit Britain in the winter. Birds like Bewick's swans and pink-footed geese arrive in this country in the autumn. They come from the colder north and escape even harsher conditions found there.

▶ Look at the map showing the migration routes of 4 birds.

d Which two birds do you think are summer visitors to Britain?

e Which do you think are winter visitors to Britain?

---

1 How do each of the following pass the winter:
a) hedgehog?
b) swallow?
c) greenfly?
d) Bewick's swan?

2 Some animals undergo changes in order to survive the winter.
a) Some animals like the stoat and birds like the ptarmigan have white coats in winter. Why do you think this is?
b) Many wild animals grow thick coats in winter. So do cats and dogs. Why do you think this is?

3 Discuss how you could help garden birds to survive the winter. Make a poster to encourage others to care for birds in winter.

4 Different climates have different patterns of rainfall throughout the year.
a) Plot 2 graphs using the following sets of rainfall data.

Month	Rainfall in mm	
Jan	55	60
Feb	50	80
Mar	30	170
Apr	20	250
May	15	23
June	5	120
July	0	80
Aug	0	80
Sept	20	90
Oct	20	90
Nov	50	140
Dec	60	130

b) Study the rainfall patterns shown and label your graphs with either Entebbe (tropical forest) or Alice Springs (hot desert).

Things to do

Who's eating who?

Why do you think cows, horses and sheep spend so much time eating? They eat mainly grass.
Animals that eat plants are called **herbivores**.

▶ Make a list of some other herbivores.

Animals such as lions, owls and foxes feed on meat.
We call animals that eat other animals **carnivores**.

▶ Make a list of some other carnivores.

How do you think plants feed?
Green plants get their energy from the Sun.
They are able to change light energy into chemical energy in food.
They are the only living things able to do this.
Green plants are called **producers**.

Food chains

A **food chain** shows the movement of energy between plants and animals.

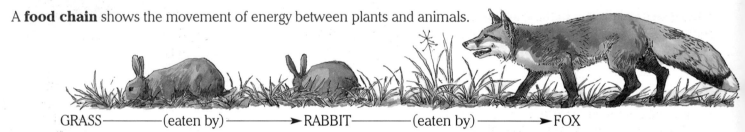

GRASS————(eaten by)————▶RABBIT————(eaten by)————▶FOX

The arrows shows the direction in which the energy flows from one to another.

Here is a food chain with 4 organisms:

GRASS————▶GRASSHOPPER————▶FIELDMOUSE————▶OWL

Notice that the food chain always begins with a producer (green plant).
This can include parts of a plant such as buds or fruits or even dead leaves.
Some animals feed only upon dead plants and animals.

DEAD LEAVES————▶WOODLOUSE————▶BLACKBIRD

You are also part of some food chains. Think of some of the things that you eat. Here is one example of a food chain that might involve you:

GRASS————▶SHEEP————▶HUMAN

▶ Write down some other food chains that include you.
Use arrows to show which way the energy is going.

▶ Look at the woodland picture at the beginning of this topic.
See how many food chains you can find. Write them down.
Use the arrows to show the direction of the food energy flow.

Looking at animals in leaf litter

Put some leaf litter into a white tray.

Carefully sort through it and collect any small animals that you find. You can pick them up with a fine paint brush or by using a pooter.

Be careful that you don't damage them.

Your teacher will give you a sheet showing what each animal eats.

Try to write down possible food chains for the leaf litter.

Wash your hands after this activity.

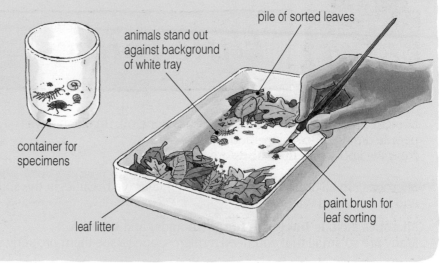

container for specimens

pile of sorted leaves

animals stand out against background of white tray

paint brush for leaf sorting

leaf litter

Food webs

Most animals will eat more than one thing. Frogs would get pretty fed up if they just ate slugs. They also eat snails and different types of insects.

A **food web** is made up of many food chains. It gives a more complete picture of how animals feed.

▶ Look at this woodland food web. Try to find all the food chains and write them down. There are 6 for you to look for.

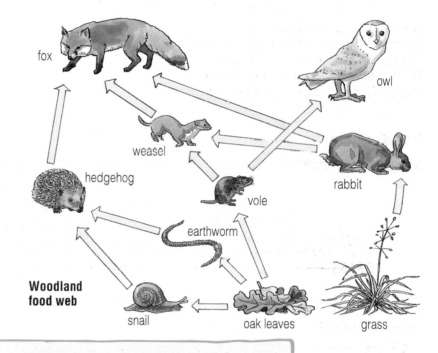

fox

owl

weasel

hedgehog

vole

rabbit

earthworm

Woodland food web

snail

oak leaves

grass

---

1 Look back at the woodland food web.
a) Name 2 carnivores from this web.
b) Name 2 herbivores from this web.
c) Name 2 producers from this web.
d) If all the foxes died, what do you think would happen to the number of:
   i) hedgehogs?   ii) snails?

2 Why does a food chain always begin with a green plant?

3 Look at these 2 food chains:

GRAIN → CHICKEN → HUMAN

GRAIN → HUMAN

Which of these food chains provides most food for people?
Why do you think this is?

4 Look at this seashore food web.

Seashore food web

sea bird

flatfish

starfish

dog whelk

mussel

barnacle

limpet

small algae

a) What do dog whelks feed on?
b) If the dog whelks were all killed by pollution, what would happen to the number of: i) flatfish?   ii) barnacles?
c) Draw a food chain with 5 organisms from this food web.
d) How many carnivores are there in this food web?

Things to do

Little rotters

Look at this photograph of food that has gone off. In olden days people did not know why food went bad.
Now we know that **microbes** are to blame.

Microbes are all around us. They are in the air we breathe, in the soil and in untreated water.

Microbes include **bacteria**, **fungi** (moulds) and **viruses**.
Many are so small that you need a microscope to see them properly.

Mould growing on some nectarines

Looking at moulds

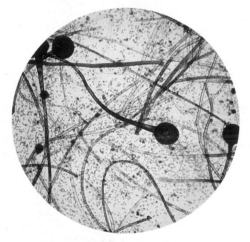

Using tweezers place a small piece of bread mould on to a slide.

Add a drop of water and gently lower a cover slip on to the mould. If it does not lie flat, gently tap the cover slip with the end of your tweezers.

▶ Look at the bread mould under your microscope.
Describe exactly what you see.

Bread mould under the microscope

Picking some mould off old bread with tweezers

Lowering cover slip onto mould on a slide

Mouldy bread!

What affects the growth of microbes?

Old bread often goes mouldy.
How could you find out what affects how quickly bread goes mouldy?

Plan an investigation.

How would you make it a fair test?
Decide how you would record your results.
Can you predict any patterns that your results might have?

▶ Which conditions do you think *stop* the following foods from going bad?

a   frozen sweetcorn.
b   dried peas.
c   vacuum-packed bacon.
d   canned peaches.
e   packet of crisps.

Something in the air?

It is now known that microbes make food go bad, but how do they reach the food in the first place?

In this experiment you are going to use **nutrient broth** to grow microbes.

In order to make it a fair test the broth must be **sterilised**. This means that any microbes already present will be killed.

Take 4 test-tubes and pour in nutrient broth to fill each to about a third full.

Set them up as shown in this diagram.

Get your teacher to heat tubes A, B, C and D to a high temperature in a pressure cooker for 15 minutes.

What do you think this will do to the nutrient broth?

Label your test-tubes. Place them in a beaker and leave them at room temperature for one week.

Copy out the table so that you are ready to record your results.

If microbes are present they will turn the broth cloudy.

f In which test-tubes did the broth turn cloudy?

g How did the microbes get to the broth in these tubes?

h Do you think microbes are lighter or heavier than air? Give your reason.

i Why did microbes not get into the broth in test-tube D?

Tube	A	B	C	D
Clear or cloudy?				

Things to do

1 The Cook family went away on their summer holiday for 3 weeks. They left some food out in the kitchen in their hurry to leave.
What do you think will have happened to each of the following foods by the time they return?

packet of cornflakes   open bottle of milk
bowl of sugar   jar of jam (with lid off)
piece of cheese   tin of grapefruit
apple   packet of salted peanuts
bowl of cat meat

2 Find out about 3 microbes that are harmful to people and 3 microbes that are useful.

3 Many food packets have 'sell by' or 'use by' dates on them.
Make a list of some of the foods that are marked with these dates.
What do you think might happen to the food after this date?
Canned and dried foods don't need a 'sell by' date. Why is this?

4 Louis Pasteur was a French scientist famous for his work on microbes. Find out about his work using ROMs, the internet and books.

Ashes to ashes

We have already seen that microbes can make food go rotten.
Microbes can also make dead plants and animals rot.
Instead of saying they rot, we could say they **decompose**.
We call microbes which can make dead things rot **decomposers**.
They can digest dead things just as we digest our food.

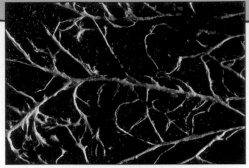
Fungus growing on compost

Heaps of microbes!

Have you seen a **compost heap** in a garden?
This is a place where dead plant material is put. Microbes grow
well here and rot down the plant material to form a compost.
Gardeners dig the compost into the soil to improve it for growing
plants.

▶ Look at this diagram of a compost heap.

a Why do you think the heap has holes in the sides and base?

b Why do you think the heap has a lid?

c The heap is sometimes turned with a fork. Why is this?

d It is important that the heap is kept moist but not soaking.
Why do you think this is?

e The heap rots quicker in summer than in winter. Why is this?

f What conditions do you think are needed for decay by microbes
to occur?

A compost heap

lid
rotten leaves
hole
broken bricks

A lot of rot or not?

Things that rot are **biodegradable**.

Materials that never rot are **non-biodegradable**.

▶ Look at this photograph.

g Which of the items shown do you think are biodegradable?

h Why do non-biodegradable materials cause problems for
our environment?

▶ How do you think the following non-biodegradable items
might harm wildlife?

i Broken glass on a path.

j A milk bottle in a hedge.

k Angler's lead weights in a pond.

l Lost plastic fishing nets in the sea.

Finding out which microbes rot grass

Take 3 petri-dishes containing sterile agar jelly. The jelly is a food for microbes.

Label your dishes A, B and C.

Using sterile tweezers add some boiled grass to dish A,
                         add some freshly cut grass to dish B,
                         leave dish C unopened.

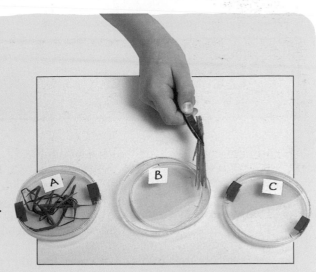

Use sticky tape to fix the lid of each dish to its base.

Place them in an incubator at 25 °C and leave them for a few days.

After a few days look for any sign that microbes are present. Do not open the dishes.

m Why was the grass in dish A boiled first?

n Why was dish C left unopened?

o Why were the dishes kept at 25 °C?

Dig this!

You can find out which things are biodegradable just by burying them in the soil. If you dig them up at different times afterwards you can see if they are rotting.

Plan an investigation to see which things rot and how fast they rot.

What sort of things would you use?
Your teacher can help you with some suggestions.

How often would you dig up and examine the things that you bury?

How could you measure and record how much of anything had rotted?

Can you predict any patterns that your results might have?

---

1 Sometimes dead things do not decompose. Say why you think each of the following did not rot.

a) In Siberia the bodies of animals called mammoths have been found in frozen ground. They are thousands of years old.

b) Human bodies (hundreds of years old) have been found in acid peat bogs.

c) The ancient Egyptians buried their kings as mummies. This involved drying out the body in a burial chamber to preserve it.

2 The hard parts of animals sometimes do not decay. They may be preserved as fossils. Find out how this can take place and write a brief report.

3 A farmer wants to preserve grass to feed her animals in the winter. She can do this in two ways. Either she can pack it tightly in a large container so that air cannot get in (this makes silage), or she can dry the grass out to make hay.
Explain why:
a) silage, and
b) hay
do not rot.

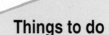
Things to do

Questions

1 Choose: a) an insect b) a bird and c) a mammal.
For each of your choices, say where it lives (its habitat), what it
feeds on and how it is adapted to its habitat.

2 George says: "when I dig my compost, steam comes out of it".
Plan an investigation to find out how much heat is given off by
rotting grass.
You can use the sort of equipment found in your science laboratory.
Remember to make your investigation a fair test. Do not try out your
plan unless you have checked it with your teacher.

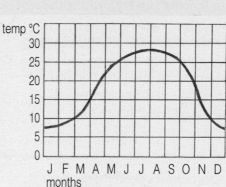

3 See if you can make a food chain out of these:
a) thrush, cabbage, caterpillar
b) slug, hedgehog, lettuce
c) tiny plants, fish, water fleas, tadpoles
d) greenfly, blackbird, ladybird, rose bush.

4 Look at the 3 temperature graphs below.
a) See if you can match them up with London, Singapore and Alaska.
b) Give a reason for your choice in each case.
c) Which of these places do you think would be the most difficult
    for plants and animals to survive in? Give your reasons.

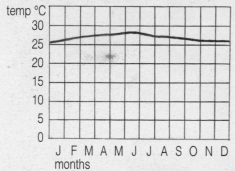
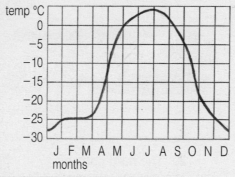
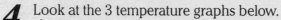

5 I am a microbe. I really like rotting things down.
I live in Mouldy Manor, which has just been deserted by its owners.
Write about my decaying adventures.

6 Some pupils did a survey of a small woodland
habitat. They identified and counted all the
trees. The table shows their results.
a) Draw a bar-chart of these results.
b) Which were the 2 most common trees
    in the wood?

Name of tree	Number in wood
ash	8
beech	15
birch	20
holly	2
oak	4

7 Milk can be preserved in a number of ways:
a) pasteurised b) sterilised c) ultra-high temperature (UHT).
Find out about each of these methods.
Why does pasteurised milk turn sour even in a sealed bottle?
Why do sterilised and UHT milk keep so long in their containers?

Earth and Space

15

Here is a photo of our beautiful planet Earth.
It is one of the 9 planets that go round the Sun.

Our Sun is just one of the billions of stars in our galaxy.

And our galaxy is just one of the billions of galaxies in our Universe . . . .

Each morning, the Sun rises in the East.

a In which direction does it set at dusk?

b In which direction is it at mid-day?

c Why must you never look straight at the Sun?

d In winter, is the day-time shorter or longer than in summer?

e In winter, is the Sun higher or lower in the sky?

f What would happen on Earth if the Sun stopped shining?

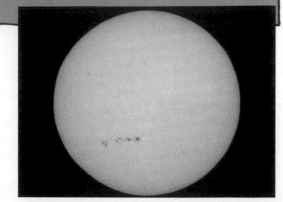

The Sun – our nearest star. On the same scale, the Earth is about the size of this full stop.

Day and night

Use a ball and a lamp (or a torch) to find out why we get day and night:

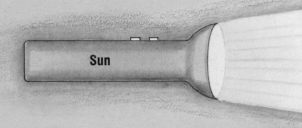

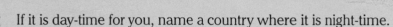

Sun

Earth

g If it is day-time for you, name a country where it is night-time.

h How many hours does it take for the Earth to spin round once?

i Which way does the Earth spin so that the Sun 'rises' in the East?

A year

Use a ball and a lamp to find out how the Earth moves in orbit round the Sun:

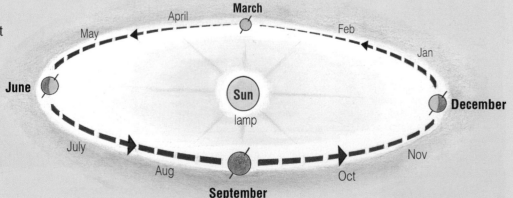

j How long does it take for the Earth to make one complete journey round the Sun?

k How many times does the Earth spin on its axis while it makes this journey?

l You are held on to the Earth by the force of gravity. What force do you think keeps the Earth in orbit round the Sun?

handwritten top right p 2
level B
1.9

$23\frac{1}{2}°$

axis

The 4 seasons

► Look at these 4 photos.

m Which season (winter, spring, summer, autumn) is shown in each one?

We have different seasons because the Earth's axis is **tilted**.
The axis is tilted at $23\frac{1}{2}°$, like this:

As the Earth moves round the Sun, **it is always tilted the same way**,
like this:

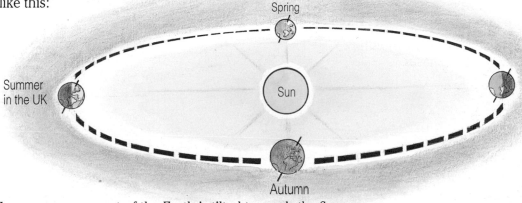

Spring

Summer
in the UK

Sun

Winter
in the UK

Autumn

In summer, our part of the Earth is tilted towards the Sun.
The Sun appears to be higher in the sky, and daylight lasts longer.
So it is warmer.
In winter, our part of the Earth is tilted away from the Sun.
The Sun is lower in the sky, and the day time is shorter. So it is colder.

Use the ball and lamp to show the 4 seasons. Mark your position on the ball, and watch it carefully as the Earth goes round the Sun. (Remember to keep the ball tilted in the same direction all the time.)

► Imagine you are at the North pole. At what time of the year is it

n daylight for 24 hours?

o night-time for 24 hours?

1 Copy and complete:
a) A day is the time for the . . . . to . . . .
once on its axis.
b) A year is the time it takes for the . . . . to
travel once round the . . . .
c) In one year there are . . . . days.
d) The Earth's axis is tilted at an angle of . . . .
e) In summer, our part of the . . . . is tilted
towards the . . . . , so the Sun appears
. . . . in the sky and the days are . . . . and
warmer.

2 A scarecrow, 1 metre high, is
standing in the middle of a field.
Write down as many things
as you can about its shadow,
a) in summer, b) in winter.

3 How would our lives be different if:
a) The Earth was much closer to the Sun?
b) The Earth turned more slowly on its
axis?
c) The Earth's axis was not tilted at all?

Things to do

15b The Earth and the Moon

Full Moon

An astronaut on the Moon

▶ Look at the photos:

a Write down 5 things that you know about the Moon.

b Would you like to live on the Moon? Why?

c The Moon shines at night, but it is not hot like the Sun. Where do you think the light comes from?

The Moon moves in an orbit round the Earth.
It is held in this orbit by the pull of gravity.
One complete orbit of the Moon takes about 1 month (1 'moonth').

The Moon looks different at different times of the month.
It has **phases**. A 'full moon' is one of the phases.

Phases of the Moon

Use a lamp and 2 balls to investigate the phases of the Moon:

The numbers 1–8 show 8 different positions of the Moon round the Earth. They are about 4 days apart.

At each position, look at the Moon from the position of the Earth. That is, from the **centre** of the circle.

On this diagram, some parts of the Moon are coloured yellow. These are the parts in sunlight that you can see from the Earth.

- Sketch what you see in each position when you are at the centre of the circle. Label your sketches with the correct names of the phases:

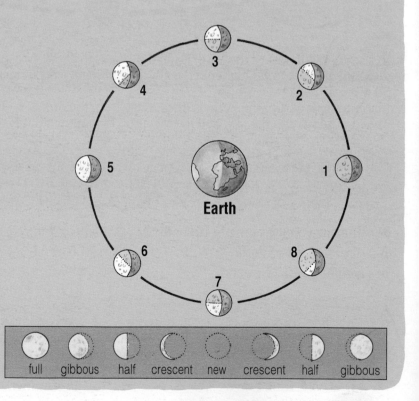

Sun

sunlight

Earth

full   gibbous   half   crescent   new   crescent   half   gibbous

Observing the Moon

Your teacher will give you a Help Sheet on which you can record your observations of the Moon for the next month.

186

Eclipse of the Moon   (lunar eclipse)

When you stand in sunlight, there is a shadow behind you.
In the same way, there is a big shadow behind the Earth.
If the Moon moves into this shadow, we call it an **eclipse** of the Moon:

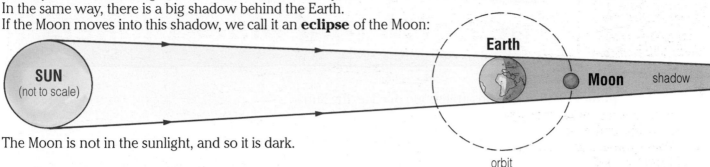

The Moon is not in the sunlight, and so it is dark.

Eclipse of the Sun   (solar eclipse)

This happens when the Moon comes directly between the Sun and the
Earth. Part of the Earth is in the Moon's shadow.
The sky goes dark even though it is day-time, because the Moon is
blocking out the Sun's rays.
In a total eclipse, only the flames round the edge of the Sun can be seen.

Total solar eclipse

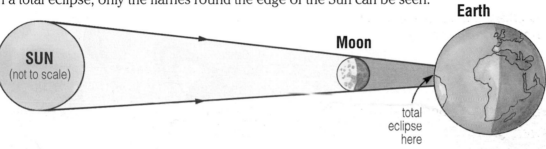

Use a lamp and 2 balls to show:
1) an eclipse of the Moon, and   2)   an eclipse of the Sun.

The Moon is covered in craters. We think they were caused by
large rocks from space, crashing into the Moon.
These rocks are called **metcorites**.

Design an investigation to find out what changes the *size and
shape of craters*. (Hint: you could use sand and marbles.)

Plan the investigation, and if you have time, do it.

1   Copy and complete:
a)   The Moon takes one . . . . to go round
the . . . . In each position it looks
different to us, with different . . . .
b)   In an eclipse of the Moon, the Moon
moves into the shadow of the . . . .
c)   In an eclipse of the Sun, the . . . . blocks
out the light from the . . . . so that the
. . . . is in a shadow.

2   Design a Moon-station for an astronaut
to live in. Draw a plan and label all the
important features.

3   Draw a diagram of the Earth and Moon
to a scale of: 1 mm = 1000 miles.

Earth–Moon distance	=	240 000 miles
Earth's diameter	=	8000 miles
Moon's diameter	=	2000 miles

The Sun is 93 000 000 miles away, and
900 000 miles in diameter. Where would
the Sun be on your diagram?

4   Write a story about a voyage to the
Moon. Describe some of the difficulties
you would have to overcome.

Things to do

The Earth and other planets

15c

The Earth is a **planet**. It travels in an orbit round our star, the Sun.

a Which is bigger: the Sun or the Earth?
b How long does it take for the Earth to make 1 orbit of the Sun?

The Earth is one of a 'family' of 9 planets. All of them are orbiting round the Sun. This is the **Solar System**.

The 9 planets are different sizes:

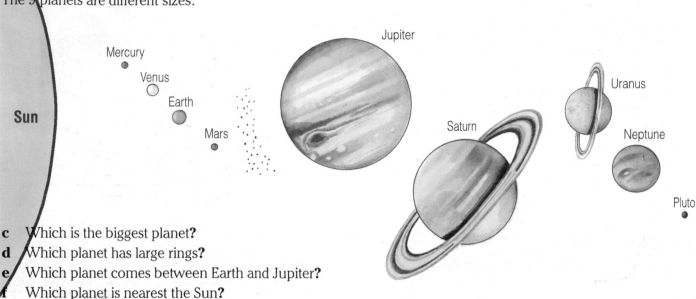

c Which is the biggest planet?
d Which planet has large rings?
e Which planet comes between Earth and Jupiter?
f Which planet is nearest the Sun?
g Which planet is farthest from the Sun?
h Which planet do you think will be the coldest?

Here are some data on the planets:

	Mercury	Venus	Earth	Mars	Asteroids	Jupiter	Saturn	Uranus	Neptune	Pluto
Diameter (km)	5000	12 000	12 800	7000	–	140 000	120 000	52 000	50 000	3000
Distance from the Sun (million km)	60	110	150	230	–	780	1400	2900	4500	6000
Time to travel 1 orbit round the Sun (years)	0.2	0.6	1	2	–	12	30	84	160	250

i Which planet is almost the same size as the Earth?
j Which planets are larger than the Earth?
k Which planet moves round the Sun in the shortest time?
l What pattern can you see between the *distance* from the Sun and the *time* taken for 1 orbit?
m What are the asteroids?

How far apart are the planets?

The distances between the planets are huge – much farther than the diagram on the opposite page shows.

Here is a scale diagram of the distances to the planets:

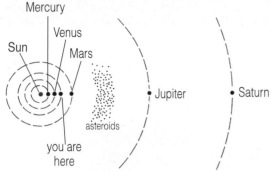
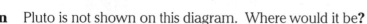

n Pluto is not shown on this diagram. Where would it be?

o Write down the names of the 4 inner planets.

p Why are these inner planets hotter than the 5 outer planets?

q Would the Sun look bigger or smaller from Mercury?

r Would the Sun look bright or dim from Pluto?

s What is the name of the force that holds the planets in orbit round the Sun?

t The orbit of each planet is not quite a circle. It is an **ellipse**. Draw an ellipse.

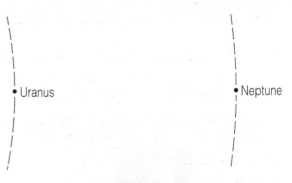

The Voyager-2 space probe

Make a scale model of the Solar System

1 For the Sun use a grapefruit or a cardboard disc with a diameter of 11 cm.

2 For the Earth make a small ball of plasticine just 1 mm across.
Make all the other planets to the same scale, using the table below:

3 Hold your 'Earth' at a distance of 12 metres from your 'Sun'. Use the table to hold all the other planets at the correct distances.
You will need to go on the playing field!

On this scale the nearest star would be another grapefruit, about 3000 kilometres away!

	Mercury	Venus	Earth	Mars	Asteroids	Jupiter	Saturn	Uranus	Neptune	Pluto
Size of 'planet'	$\frac{1}{2}$ mm	1 mm	1 mm	$\frac{1}{2}$ mm		11 mm	9 mm	4 mm	4 mm	$\frac{1}{4}$ mm
Distance from 'Sun'	5 m	8 m	12 m	18 m		60 m	110 m	220 m	350 m	460 m

1 Copy and complete:
a) There are . . . . planets in the . . . . System.
b) The names of the 9 planets (in order) are:
c) The coldest planet is . . . . This is because it is the farthest from the . . . .

2 Why do you think Pluto was the last planet to be discovered?

3 What do you think it would be like to live on Mercury?

4 Plot a bar-chart of the diameters of the planets, using a spreadsheet if possible.

5 For the first 5 planets, plot a line-graph of the **time** taken to travel 1 orbit round the Sun against the **distance** from the Sun.

The asteroids are large rocks that travel round the Sun at an average distance of 400 million km. Use your graph to estimate how long they take to make 1 orbit.

Things to do

The Solar System

▶ Use the information on these two pages to fill in a table like this one:

Planet	Type of surface	Average temperature	Type of atmosphere	Length of a 'day'	Moons, rings
Mercury					

Mercury is a small planet, about the size of our Moon. It has a rocky surface which is covered in craters.

It has no atmosphere. The side facing the Sun is very hot (about 430 °C, hot enough to melt lead).

From space, **Earth** is a blue planet with swirls of cloud. It is the only planet with water and oxygen and living things.

It is at the right distance from the Sun, with the right chemicals, to support life. Of course, other stars in the Universe may have planets with the same conditions.

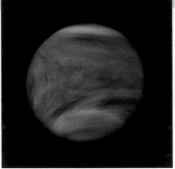

Venus is almost as big as the Earth, but it is very unpleasant. Its rocky surface is covered by thick clouds of sulphuric acid.

The atmosphere is mainly carbon dioxide. This traps the Sun's heat (by the 'Greenhouse Effect') so that Venus is even hotter than Mercury.

Mars – the red planet – is a dry cold desert of red rocks, with huge mountains and canyons. No life has been found on Mars.

It has a thin atmosphere of carbon dioxide, and 2 small moons. Mars was the first of the planets to be visited by one of our space-craft.

Planet	Diameter (km)	Distance to Sun (million km)	Time for 1 orbit (planet's 'year')	Time for 1 spin (planet's 'day')	Average temperature on sunny side (°C)	Moons
Mercury	5000	60	88 days	1400 hours	+430	0
Venus	12 000	110	220 days	5800 hours	+470	0
Earth	12 800	150	$365\frac{1}{4}$ days	24 hours	+20	1
Mars	7000	230	2 years	25 hours	−20	2
Asteroids						
Jupiter	140 000	780	12 years	10 hours	−150	16
Saturn	120 000	1400	30 years	10 hours	−180	*18 + rings
Uranus	52 000	2900	84 years	17 hours	−210	15 + rings
Neptune	50 000	4500	160 years	16 hours	−220	8
Pluto	3000	6000	250 years	150 hours	−230	1

199

* Cassini flyby + other recent observation indicate 47 moons

Jupiter is the largest planet, and is very cold. It has no solid surface. It is mainly liquid hydrogen and helium, surrounded by these gases and clouds. The Giant Red Spot is a huge storm, 3 times the size of Earth. Jupiter has 16 moons.

Saturn is another 'gas giant', very like Jupiter. The beautiful rings are not solid. They are made of billions of chunks of ice and rock. They are held in orbit by the pull of Saturn's gravity.

Uranus is another 'gas giant', made of hydrogen and helium.
Unlike the other planets it is lying on its side as it goes round the Sun.
It was discovered in 1781 by William Herschel.

Neptune is very like Uranus. It is a blue 'gas giant'. The Great Dark Spot is a storm the size of Earth.

a Which planet is most like the Earth? Explain your reasons.

b Why is it hard for scientists to find out about i) Venus? ii) Pluto?

c Only one planet has liquid water on its surface. Why is this?

Pluto is the smallest planet, discovered in 1930.
It is a rocky planet, covered in ice. It has a very thin atmosphere of methane.

America is planning to send astronauts to Mars.
It would cost billions of dollars. Do you think it is worth it?

Discuss this in your group, and write down the arguments for and against.

1 Imagine that you are an advertising agent for holidays in the year 2030. Choose one of the planets (not Earth) and:
a) make up an advertising slogan for it,
b) draw a poster or write a TV commercial for it.

2 Write a story about 'A journey through the Solar System'.

3 Explain why you think life developed on Earth and not on other planets.

4 Which planets have a thin atmosphere or none at all?
Use your data to see if it has anything to do with size.
Can you think of a reason for this?

Things to do

Our place in the Universe

Our Sun is a **star**. It is like all the others you can see in the night sky. In size, the Sun is just an average star.

The star patterns you can see at night are called **constellations**.
For example, the Plough (or Great Bear) looks like this:

▶ Write down the names of any constellations that you know of. Your teacher may give you a star-map of the constellations.

The Sun is part of a huge collection of stars called a **galaxy**. Our galaxy is called the Milky Way. It is a collection of more than 100 000 million stars!

Our galaxy has a *spiral* shape. We are in one of the spiral arms:

Our galaxy is huge. It takes light just 8 minutes to travel from the Sun to Earth, but it takes 100 000 years for light to travel across our galaxy!

A **light-year** is the *distance* that light travels in one year. And light travels at a speed of 300 000 kilometres per second!

Radio waves also travel at the speed of light. Nothing can travel faster than this.

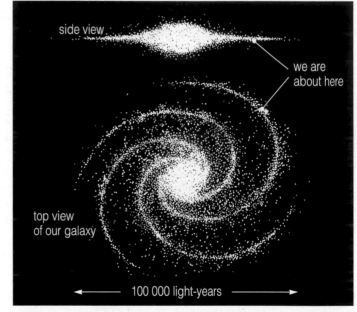

side view

we are about here

top view of our galaxy

◀— 100 000 light-years —▶

Our galaxy, the Milky Way

Other galaxies

The Milky Way is our galaxy, but it is not the only galaxy. It is one of a group of 20 galaxies called the **Local Group**.
The Andromeda galaxy is one of these:

Through telescopes we can see *millions* of other galaxies!
All the galaxies together, and the space between them, form the **Universe**.

Some galaxies are so far away that it has taken the light 10 000 million years to reach us. So we see them as they *were*, 10 000 million years ago!

So the Universe is even older than this.

The Andromeda galaxy.
It contains 300 billion stars and is
2 million light-years away from us.

The expanding Universe

In 1929, Edwin Hubble discovered that the galaxies are moving apart. The Universe is expanding!

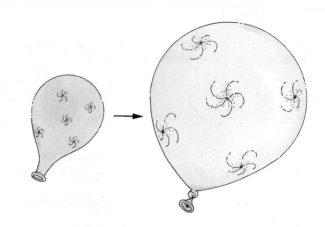

This is rather like a balloon which has some ink-marks on it. The ink-marks represent the galaxies. The balloon is the Universe. As the balloon is blown up, the Universe expands and all the galaxies move farther apart.
This is a 'model' of our expanding Universe.

Thinking back in time, the Universe was once very small. Astronomers believe it started about 12 000 million years ago, in an explosion called the **Big Bang**. *15 000*
It has been expanding ever since.

Your place in the Universe

Your teacher will give you a Help Sheet for this.
Cut out the pictures and sort them into the right order.
This will show you how you fit into the Universe.

- What is your full address in the Universe?

Making a telescope

To look at the Universe, an astronomer uses a **telescope**.

You can make a telescope by using 2 lenses, like this:

Look through the lenses, and move the thin lens along the ruler until you see a sharp image.

- What do you notice about the image that you see?

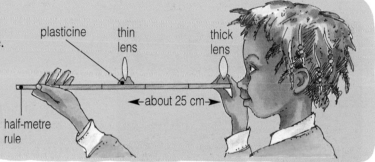

plasticine · thin lens · thick lens · about 25 cm · half-metre rule

ET ... Extra-Terrestrial

Do you think there could be other life in the Universe? Perhaps on a planet round another star?

Suppose you were going to send a 'space-capsule' on a long journey into space. It may be found by aliens some time in the future.

What would you put into the capsule to tell the aliens about yourself? (Remember: they won't understand English!)

---

1 Copy and complete:
a) The Sun is really an ordinary .... It is part of our ...., called the Milky Way.
b) A light-year is the .... that light travels in one ....
c) The Universe has been .... since the time of the ....

2 The speed of light is 300 000 km/s. How far, in kilometres, is a light-year?

3 Here is a list of objects:
star moon galaxy planet Universe
a) Put them in order of size (smallest first).
b) For each one, write a sentence to explain what it is.

4 To travel to another star would take centuries. Sketch the design of a space-ship for this. What would be the problems for the people on board?

Things to do

Finding out about space

People have been observing the night sky since ancient times and wondering what it all means. To the ancient Greeks the patterns of stars resembled everyday objects, animals and characters from mythology.
We call these patterns of stars **constellations**.

The constellation Orion

The first **optical telescopes** were made in Holland at the start of the sixteenth century. In 1609 the famous Italian scientist Galileo had the idea of using this new invention to study the heavens. When he pointed his telescope at the planet Jupiter he was amazed to see that it had 4 moons.

▶ We now know that Jupiter has, in fact, got 16 moons. Why is it that Galileo didn't see them all**?**

Nowadays, there are many thousands of optical telescopes studying many different objects in the night sky.

The **Hubble Space Telescope** was put into orbit around the Earth in 1990.
As well as light, it can 'see' other kinds of radiation, some of which cannot be studied on Earth because they are filtered out by the Earth's atmosphere.

By analysing the light given out by stars, scientists can tell which elements exist on the star and how quickly it is moving away from the Earth.

Radio waves can also penetrate the Earth's atmosphere.
These are detected by **radio telescopes.**

In 1957 the first **artificial satellite**, Sputnik 1, was put into orbit around the Earth. By 1961 the first man, **Yuri Gagarin**, and by 1963 the first woman, **Valentina Tereshkova,** had travelled into space. They orbited the Earth for what seems now to be only a short time but these were to be the first of many exploratory flights into space.

Valentina Tereshkova

Luna 2, launched in 1959, was the first space probe to reach the **Moon**. There were many other exploratory missions to the Moon before the Apollo 11 landed the first astronaut, **Neil Armstrong**, on the Moon in 1969.

In 1977 Voyagers I and II started a space flight that might last forever. They flew past the planets, sending photographs and other valuable information back to Earth, before leaving the Solar System completely. At the start of the 21st century, now 8 billion kilometres from the Sun, they continue to transmit data from far beyond the furthest planet.

Spacecraft are very expensive to make. Since 1981 there have been many flights into space in reusable **space shuttles**. These spacecraft are powered into space by huge rockets that eventually fall away when the fuel they contain is used up. The space shuttle returns to Earth under its own power at the end of the mission, and can be used again.

Inter-planetary exploration started in 1962 with the flight of Mariner 2 to **Venus**. However, since then, **Mars** has become the focus of attention for space scientists. The first soft landing on Mars was made by the Mars 3 mission in 1971. An automated rover vehicle was eventually landed on Mars by the Mars Pathfinder in 1997. It is likely that there will be manned missions to Mars in the 21st century.

▶ Would you like to be the first person to set foot on Mars? What do you think it would feel like being somewhere that no-one else had ever been?

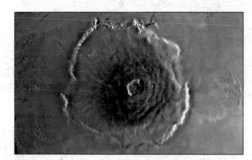

The surface of Mars

1 Early space flights involved either the USSR (Soviet Russia) or the USA (America). Copy the following and find out from which country each came.
a) Sputnik 1   e) Luna 2
b) Valentina Tereshkova   f) Mariner 2
c) Voyager I   g) Neil Armstrong
d) Mars Pathfinder   h) Yuri Gagarin

2 Draw a time-line to show how space exploration has developed using the dates given in the text.

3 Galileo's observations of the moons around Jupiter eventually got him into trouble with the Catholic Church in Rome. Find out more about Galileo (Galileo Galilei) and the trouble he had.

4 'Houston, we have a problem.' These were the words of Apollo 13 commander Jack Swigert on 13th April 1970. An oxygen tank had exploded and the astronauts had to conserve power, air and water for four tense days before the rocket could be brought back to Earth.

Apollo 13: the film

Imagine that you are one of the astronauts on Apollo 13. Write about what it must have been like during those four days.

Things to do

Questions

1 The table shows some data for the sunshine in London:

a) Explain why summer is hotter than winter.
b) Sketch the path of the Sun through the sky for
   i) a day in January, and   ii) a day in July.

Month	Altitude of midday sun	Hours of daylight
January	low, 15°	8
July	high, 62°	16

2 The table shows the times of sunrise and sunset in Edinburgh throughout the year:

Date	Jan 21	Feb 21	Mar 21	Apr 21	May 21	Jun 21	Jul 21	Aug 21	Sep 21	Oct 21	Nov 21	Dec 21
Sunrise	8.4	7.4	6.2	4.9	3.9	3.4	4.0	4.9	5.9	6.9	8.0	8.7
Sunset	16.4	17.5	18.5	19.5	20.5	21.0	20.7	19.6	18.2	17.0	15.9	15.7

(All the times are in decimal hours and GMT on a 24-hour clock)

a) On graph paper, plot the sunrise times against the date.
   Then plot the sunset times on the same diagram.
b) When is the day longest?
c) When is the day shortest?
d) When is the day-time equal in length to the night?

3 The photo shows the first astronaut to land on the Moon:

a) Describe first of all what you can see in the photo.
   These are your *observations*.

b) Then write down what *conclusions* you can make from:
   i)   his clothes,
   ii) his shadow,
   iii) the black sky,
   iv) his foot-marks,
   v)   his small space-craft,
   vi) the label under the photograph.

Neil Armstrong, 1969

4 Some pupils are thinking and hypothesizing:

Ayesha says, "I think that the farther a planet is from the Sun, the cooler it is."
Danielle says, "I think that the larger a planet is, the more moons it has."
Chris says, "I think that the farther a planet is from the Sun, the longer the time for 1 orbit (the planet's 'year')."

Do the data in the table on page 190 support any of these hypotheses? Explain your thinking. If you can, draw graphs to show how the data agree with the hypotheses.

5 Using a book, a ROM or the internet, write a paragraph about each of these:
a) a supernova,   b) a neutron star (pulsar),   c) a black hole,   d) a quasar.

6 In 1670, Blaise Pascal, a French scientist, wrote "Le silence éternel de ces espaces infinis m'effraie" (*The eternal silence of these infinite spaces terrifies me*).
Write a poem of your thoughts about space.

Elements

16

Your life is full of elements.
You are made of them.
You eat them. You drink them.
You are surrounded by them.

In this topic you can find out more about elements.
What are they made of?
What can we make from them?

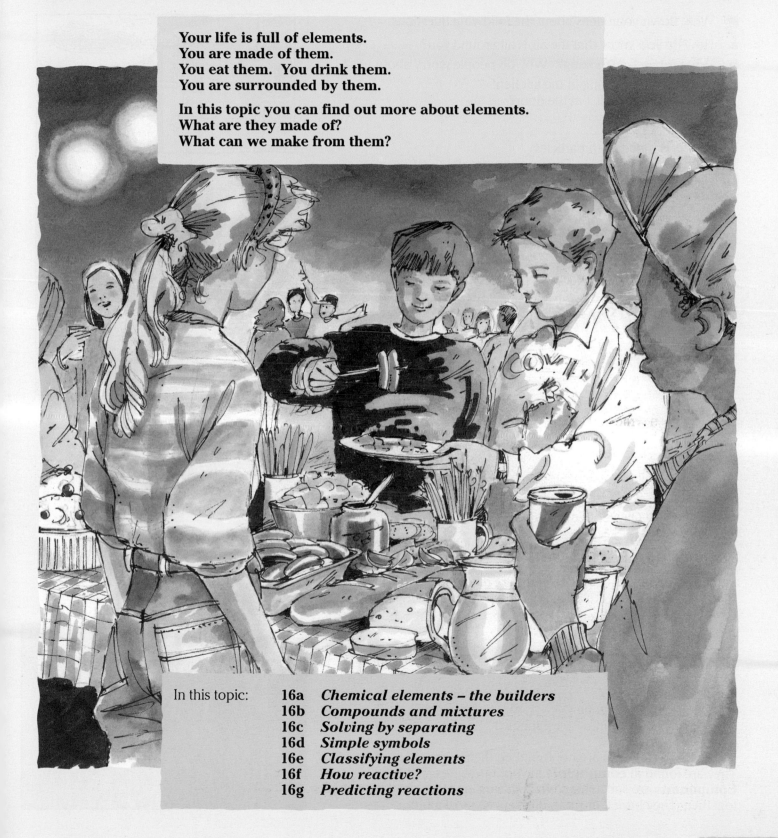

In this topic:

Chemical elements – the builders

▶ Write down your ideas about the following questions:

a How do you know that the air is all around you?

b What is passive smoking? Why do people worry about this?

c Something is cooking in the kitchen!
Why can you smell it at the door?

Everything is made from particles.
The particles are invisible. They are very small.
They are called **atoms**.
Atoms are the smallest parts of any substance.
They make up solids, liquids and gases.
If a substance is made of only one type of atom, it is a *simple substance*.
We call it an **element**. **Elements** can be solids, liquids or gases.

A copper coil

Mercury liquid

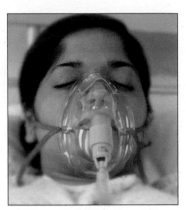

Oxygen gas

Elements are substances which *cannot be broken down into anything simpler*. **Elements** have *only one type of atom*.

You can show atoms like this:

⬤ ⬤   All the atoms which make up oxygen gas are the same as each other.
oxygen atoms   Oxygen is an **element**.

🔘 🔘   All the atoms which make up nitrogen gas are the same as each other.
nitrogen atoms   Nitrogen is an **element**.

. . . *But* remember . . . oxygen atoms are different to nitrogen atoms.
Oxygen and nitrogen are *different* elements.

Your body is made up of many elements. Some of these are:

calcium	carbon	chlorine	hydrogen
magnesium	nitrogen	oxygen	phosphorus
potassium	sodium	sulphur	

Mostly these elements are not found on their own.
They are found in **compounds** in your body.
Compounds are substances which have 2 or more elements joined together. They have 2 or more different types of atom.

Compounds look different to the elements they are made from.

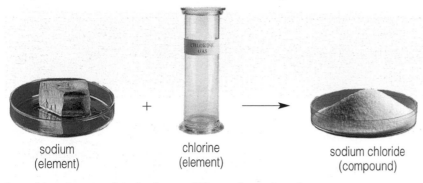

sodium (element) + chlorine (element) → sodium chloride (compound)

Compounds can also **behave** differently to the elements they are made from.

▶ Watch carefully as your teacher adds the **elements** sodium and chlorine to water. What do you see?
What happens when sodium chloride, a **compound**, is added to water?

⚠ safety glasses and screen

▶ Look at the names of these common compounds. Which elements are they made from?

sodium chloride   carbon dioxide   hydrogen oxide (water)

Finding out about limestone

Limestone is a common rock. It is a compound.
You may find some near where you live.
Use books or a computer to find out about this compound.

Which elements make up limestone?
What are the **properties** of the elements?
What are the **properties** of limestone?
What is limestone used for?

Things to do

1 Copy and complete:
All substances are made of very small particles called . . . .
Substances which contain only one type of . . . . are called . . . .
. . . . cannot be broken down into anything simpler. When these combine together, they make . . . .

2 Look at labels on foods at home. Make a list of elements and compounds that the foods contain.

3 If you discovered a new element, what would you call it?

4 Say whether each of the following is an element or a compound:

chlorine   magnesium   iron
sulphur dioxide   sulphur
carbon dioxide   iron chloride
calcium   carbon   sodium

5 The first scientist to suggest the name element was Robert Boyle. The year was 1661. Find out some information about Boyle.

Compounds and mixtures

Elements have only one type of atom.
Compounds have 2 or more *different* atoms joined together.

▶ Write down the names of 4 elements.
Write down the names of 4 compounds.

Which is the element? Which is the compound?

Atoms can join together. They make **molecules**.

2 oxygen atoms can join together. They make an oxygen **molecule**.
A carbon atom can join to 2 oxygen atoms. They make a **molecule**
of carbon dioxide.
Notice that you can have molecules of an *element* or molecules of
a *compound*.

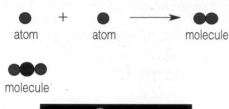

Water is a **compound**. It is made from the **elements** hydrogen
and oxygen. The **elements** combine to make the **compound**.
You can use pictures to show this:

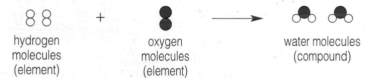

Why can't you **see** water molecules?

Spotting elements and compounds

Look at these diagrams of atoms and molecules.
Match the answers to the boxes.

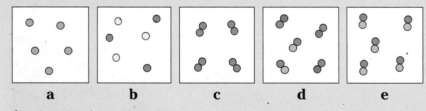

| a | b | c | d | e |

...I don't think he's an element!

i)   Atoms of one element.
ii) Molecules of one element.
iii) Molecules of one compound.
iv) A mixture of 2 elements.
v)   A mixture of 2 compounds.

We can divide all substances into 2 groups:

pure substances   or   **mixtures**

A **pure substance** contains just one element or just one compound.
A **mixture** has two (or more) elements or compounds in it.
These are just *mixed* together. They are not joined together.
If you have a **mixture** you can separate it into pure substances.
Sometimes this is easy to do. Sometimes it is hard to do.

Could you sort out the sweets in this mixture?

Separating mixtures

Think about the following mixtures. Discuss them in your group. Say what experiments you would do to separate the parts of the mixture in each case. Ask your teacher for a Help Sheet if you get stuck!

Mixture 1 – A mixed bag!
Get the raisins from the mixed fruit.

Mixture 2 – An attractive problem!
Get the iron from the sulphur powder.

Mixture 3 – Mud in the garden!
Get dry soil from the water.

Mixture 4 – Swimming makes you thirsty!
Get pure water from salty water.

Mixture 5 – A broken sugar bowl!
Get the pieces of glass from the sugar.

Mixture 6 – Colours unmixed!
Get the red dye from the purple mixture.

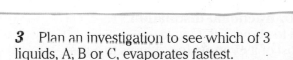

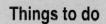

Your teacher may let you try some of these experiments.

Things to do

1 Use your own colours for atoms.
Draw 4 different boxes to show:
a) a mixture of 3 elements,
b) a pure compound,
c) a pure element,
d) a mixture of 2 compounds.

2 Draw a table like this:

Element	Mixture	Compound

Put these words in the correct columns.

magnesium   air   hydrogen   water
salty water   iron oxide   chlorine
sulphur   lemonade

3 Plan an investigation to see which of 3 liquids, A, B or C, evaporates fastest.

4 Match each word with its description.

Word	Description
element	made when atoms join together
molecule	one of 3 states of matter
evaporate	has only one type of atom
liquid	change from liquid to gas
condense	change from solid to liquid
melt	change from gas to liquid

5 Rock salt is salt from the ground. It contains particles of salt mixed with sand, dirt and other rocks.
Say how you would get a pure sample of dry salt from the rock salt.
Draw diagrams of any apparatus you would use.

Solving by separating

In the last lesson you found out some ways to separate mixtures.
Can you remember some of them?

▶ The sentences **a** to **d** should tell you about separating mixtures.
But the words are mixed up! Rearrange the words in each
sentence so that it makes sense.
Write out each correct sentence.

a insoluble Filtering separates liquid solid from.

b sea water from pure water Distillation gets.

c Chromatography coloured dyes a mixture in separates.

d separates magnet iron A from mixture a.

One of the most important mixtures to separate is crude oil.
Crude oil is a fossil fuel. It is found underground.
What does it look like?

Crude oil is *not* one pure substance. It is a **mixture** of many
different chemicals. The chemicals are very useful to us.

▶ Make a list of some of the uses of crude oil.
Life would be difficult without crude oil.
Write about some of the things which would be most difficult
for you.

Crude oil is separated by **fractional distillation**.
The crude oil is heated to about 350 °C.
At this temperature most of it **evaporates** (it turns to a gas).
The hot mixture is put into a huge tower.
It cools as it rises up the tower. The separate liquids in the mixture
collect at different temperatures (boiling points). The boiling point
is the temperature when the gas turns back to liquid.

e Is the tower hotter at the top or the bottom?

f What temperature does kerosine collect at?

Fractional distillation can separate mixtures of
other liquids. It works if the liquids have different
boiling points.

Some liquids don't mix together. Another method is used to
separate them. Think about oil and water.

▶ Design a piece of apparatus to separate oil and water.
Label all the parts. Explain how it works.

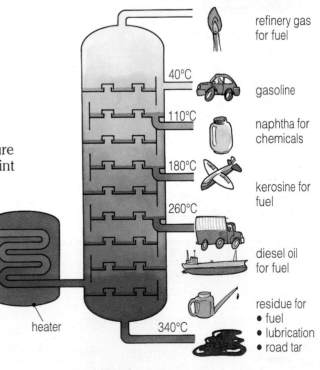

refinery gas
for fuel

40°C   gasoline

110°C   naphtha for
chemicals

180°C   kerosine for
fuel

260°C   diesel oil
for fuel

crude
oil

heater   340°C

residue for
• fuel
• lubrication
• road tar

You can see that crude oil contains lots of
useful substances.

Being able to separate the substances in crude oil solves a big problem for the world. Can you be a problem-solver?

The people who have received these two memos need a bit of help. See if you can solve the problems using separating methods.

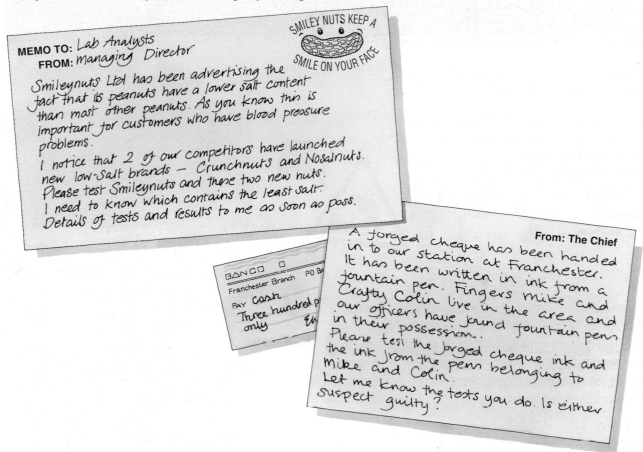

SMILEY NUTS KEEP A SMILE ON YOUR FACE

MEMO TO: Lab Analysts
FROM: Managing Director

Smileynuts Ltd has been advertising the fact that its peanuts have a lower salt content than most other peanuts. As you know this is important for customers who have blood pressure problems.

I notice that 2 of our competitors have launched new low-salt brands – Crunchnuts and Nosalnuts. Please test Smileynuts and these two new nuts. I need to know which contains the least salt. Details of tests and results to me as soon as poss.

From: The Chief

A forged cheque has been handed in to our station at Franchester. It has been written in ink from a fountain pen. Fingers Mike and Crafty Colin live in the area and our officers have found fountain pens in their possession. Please test the forged cheque ink and the ink from the pens belonging to Mike and Colin. Let me know the tests you do. Is either suspect guilty?

BANCO
Franchester Branch   PO Bo
PAY Cash
Three hundred p
only   Ei

---

1 Which substance in crude oil is used to:
a) power cars?
b) make medicines?
c) power aeroplanes?
d) make roads?
e) power lorries?

2 An orange-flavoured fruit drop is bright orange in colour. Describe an experiment to find out if the fruit drop contains orange food colouring or a mixture of red and yellow food colourings.

3 Look at the diagram. It shows the simple apparatus you could use in the laboratory to separate the liquids in crude oil.
a) Explain how the liquid is transferred from the heated tube to the collecting test tube.
b) Why is the collecting test-tube in a beaker of cold water?
c) Why is a thermometer used?
d) Why is the mineral wool used?
e) What safety measures would you take in this experiment?

Things to do

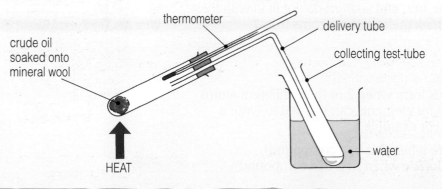

thermometer
delivery tube
crude oil soaked onto mineral wool
collecting test-tube
water
HEAT

Simple symbols

Often a symbol or picture gives information quicker than lots of writing.

▶ Test yourself on the following examples.
What do the symbols mean?

Elements

Chemists have a shorthand way of writing about elements.
They use **symbols** instead of writing out the names.

▶ Copy out the table. Fill in your guess for each element's symbol.
Then use the Help Sheet from your teacher to find out the correct answers.

Element	My guess for the symbol	Correct answer
carbon		
sulphur		
nitrogen		
oxygen		
fluorine		
phosphorus		

a Copy and complete the sentence to give a simple rule for
writing the symbols for elements.
For some elements the symbol is the . . . . of the name of
the element.

Now find the symbols for:

b calcium   **c** chlorine   **d** chromium.

The names of these elements all begin with the same letter.
The symbols use a second letter from the name too.
The second letter is written as a small letter.

e The symbols for copper, iron and sodium do not fit in with these
rules. Where do you think their symbols come from?

What **Ar**e **Th**e **S**ymbol **Ru**les? (Find the elements!)

Compounds

Remember that compounds form when 2 or more different atoms
join together. The symbols for elements can be used to write a
formula for a compound. For example,

CuO is copper oxide (ox**ide** when O is in a compound)
$LiCl$ is lithium chloride (chlor**ide** when Cl is in a compound).

What do you think are the names for the following compounds?
Write them down.

f KCl   **g** CaO   **h** MgO   **i** NaCl

Some compounds have more complicated formulas.
Look at:

$CuCl_2$

This is copper chloride. The compound has 1 copper atom and
2 chlorine atoms. How can you tell this from the formula?

▶ Copy and complete the following table. The first one has been
done for you.

Name	Formula	Number of each type of atom
carbon dioxide	CO_2	1 carbon, 2 oxygen
sodium fluoride		1 sodium, 1 fluorine
	$MgCl_2$	
	$AlCl_3$	
lithium oxide	Li_2O	

International science

All the symbols for elements are international. Maybe you can't
understand the language. But you can spot the chemical elements!
How's your Russian?

Use books or ROMs to find out about one of the elements
mentioned in this Russian book.
Make a poster to show what you have found out.

Things to do

1 Copy and complete the table:

Symbol	Name
C	
Cu	
	oxygen
N	
Ca	
	iron
	sodium
	chlorine
Mg	
S	

2 a) Write down the names of 2 elements
in each case which are:
i) solids   ii) liquids   iii) gases.
b) Draw diagrams to show how the
particles of the elements are arranged in
solids, liquids and gases.

3 The table shows the approximate
percentages of different elements in rocks of
the Earth's crust.

Element	Percentage
oxygen	48
silicon	26
aluminium	8
iron	5
calcium	4
sodium	3
potassium	2
magnesium	2
other	2

Draw **either** a pie-chart **or** a bar-chart of
this information.

16e Classifying elements

▶ Look at the objects in the photograph:
  Divide them into 2 groups:
  • Those you think are made from **elements**.
  • Those you think are made from **compounds**.

Materials can be sorted into groups. We say they can be **classified**.
You can do this by testing some **properties** of the materials.

▶ Look at the properties opposite:
  How could you test for each of these?
  What equipment would you use? What would you do?

Some of these tests could be used to put **elements** into groups.

There are over 100 elements.
Some are hard to classify. Most can be put into 2 groups.
The groups are **metals** and **non-metals**.

> strength   hardness   density
> conducting electricity
> melting point   boiling point
> conducting heat

▶ Copy out the table.
  Make it at least 10 cm long and 10 cm wide.
  Fill in your ideas about the properties of metals and non-metals.
  (You could check these with your teacher.)

Property	Metal	Non-metal
appearance		
strength		
hardness		
density		
melting and boiling points		
does it conduct heat?		
does it conduct electricity?		

Are you sure it's metal?

Metal or non-metal?

Test the elements your teacher will give you.
Decide whether each element is a metal or a non-metal.

The uses of an element depend on its properties.

a Why is aluminium used to make aircraft bodies?

b Why is copper used to make saucepans?

c Why is gold used to make jewellery?

Choose the cable

Liftum Ltd is a new company. It makes cables to carry cable cars. Each cable car seats 4 people.

Can you recommend a material to use for making the cables? You could use copper, iron or aluminium. Which would be best?

In your group, discuss which factors you will need to consider.
- Write out your list of factors.
- Which material do you **think** is the best?
- Why have you chosen this one? Are you happy with your choice?

Now **plan** some tests on the 3 materials to see which **is** best.
How can you make your results reliable?

It would be important for Liftum to know how much these materials cost.
Which do you think is the cheapest? Why?
Try to find out the cost of each one.

---

1 Write down the names and symbols of:
a) 5 metals   b) 5 non-metals.

2 Make a list of words which describe metals. Then make a list of words which describe non-metals.

3 Remi has found a lump of black solid. It is light, breaks easily and doesn't conduct electricity.
Is it a metal or non-metal?

4 Some objects can be made of metal or plastic. Discuss the advantages and disadvantages of metal or plastic for each of the following:
a) ruler   c) spoon
b) window frame   d) bucket.

5 Look around the room.
a) Name 4 objects made of metal.
b) Which metals are they made from?
c) Why are the metals used to make the objects?

Things to do

How reactive?

▶ Match each of the elements in the box with one of the descriptions **a** to **f**.

a an element with the symbol U

b a metal used to make cooking foil

c a metal used for electrical wires

d a metal which is a liquid

e an element with the symbol K

f a non-metal

- potassium
- uranium
- copper
- mercury
- carbon
- aluminium

You have tested properties of many materials. For example, strength and hardness. These are **physical properties**.

The **chemical properties** of a material are also important. Does the material change easily into a new substance? Does it **react**?

Remember! The use of a material depends on its properties.

Don't make a bridge from a metal which reacts with water! Which element is best to use? Why?

Potassium is a metal. It reacts very violently with water. Potassium is stored under oil. Why do you think this is?

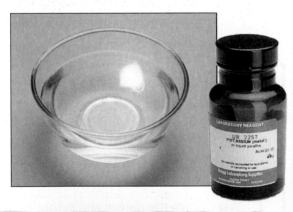

Reacting metals

Do metals react with oxygen in the air?

- Get a small piece of magnesium ribbon from your teacher. Hold it at arm's length in some tongs. Then move it into a Bunsen burner flame (air-hole just open). *Do not look directly at it*. What happens?

- Do the experiment again using copper foil rather than magnesium. What happens? Which is the more reactive, magnesium or copper?

eye protection

When metals react with oxygen they make new substances.
These are called **oxides**.

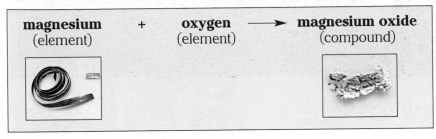

| magnesium (element) | + | oxygen (element) | → | magnesium oxide (compound) |

Metals do not all react in the same way with oxygen or with water.

Some are **_very reactive_** – potassium.
Some are **_reactive_** – magnesium.
Some are **_unreactive_** – gold.

Metals can be put in an **order of reactivity**.
The most reactive ones are at the top of the list.
The least reactive are at the bottom.

Gold is unreactive. Why don't we use gold to make bridges?

What's the order?

Plan an investigation to produce an order of reactivity for metals.
You can use any equipment you need.
Remember to always use very small amounts of chemicals when investigating.
The chemicals you can use are:

- *metal samples* – zinc, tin, magnesium, iron, copper,
- bottles of distilled (pure) water,
- bottles of dilute acid.

⚠ eye protection

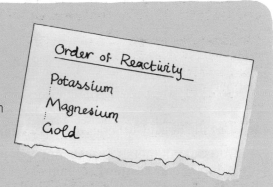

Order of Reactivity

Potassium
Magnesium
Gold

You **must** have your plan checked by your teacher.
Then do the investigation.
Write a report of your findings. Include your order of reactivity in your report. Are you **sure** your order is correct?
How could you improve this investigation?
Write down your ideas to make it better.

Things to do

1 Copy the diagram.
Put the correct words in the empty boxes.

metals compounds elements non-metals

pure substances

very reactive   reactive   unreactive

2 Use books or ROMs to find out when different metals were discovered. Make a time-chart to display in the laboratory.
Look for a pattern between the discovery dates and the metal's reactivity.

3 Amy put some metals, A, B, C and D, in water. Look at the times taken for the metals to react completely with the water:

Metal	Time (seconds)
A	15
B	35
C	5
D	no reaction

a) Which is the most reactive metal?
b) Which metal could be copper?
c) Which metal is likely to be stored under oil?
d) How could Amy have made sure this was a fair test?
e) How could she have made her results more reliable?

209

Predicting reactions

You have seen that metals can be put in order of reactivity.
This is called the **Reactivity Series**. It's a kind of League Table for metals. These tests are used to find the order.

metal + air   metal + water   metal + acid

The Reactivity Series

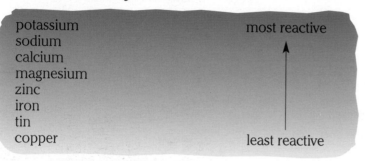

potassium	most reactive
sodium	
calcium	
magnesium	
zinc	
iron	
tin	
copper	least reactive

Can you make up your own rhymes to help you remember the order?
For example,
Please **S**top
Calling **M**y
Zebra **I**n
The **C**lass

▶ Use the Reactivity Series to help you answer these questions:

a You can put metals in acid. But your teacher will ***not*** give you samples of potassium, sodium or calcium for this. Why not?

b Where do you think gold fits in the order?

c Iron reacts slowly with water and air. What substance is made in this reaction? Do you have any examples of this at home?

d Copper does not react easily with air or water. Would it be a good idea to make cars from copper?

There is another way of finding out an order of reactivity for metals. We can set up *competitions*.
Competitions for oxygen are easy to do.

The big fight!

An experiment to heat magnesium oxide with copper is very boring. Nothing happens! There is no reaction.

Heating magnesium with copper oxide is much more exciting! There is a big reaction.

magnesium + **copper oxide** → **magnesium oxide** + **copper**
(silver-grey)   (black)   (grey-white)   (brown)

This is because magnesium is more reactive than copper. Magnesium wins the fight for the oxygen.

Reactions like this are called **displacement reactions**.
The magnesium **displaces** the copper. It pushes the copper out. It wins the oxygen.

Displacing metals

Try some other displacement experiments. See if you can spot reactions taking place. You should look to see if:
- a gas is made,
- any solids or solutions change colour,
- any solids disappear (dissolve) in solutions.

Take a spotting tray. Put **small** pieces of the 4 metals in the rows of the tray.
Use a teat pipette to add 4 different solutions to the 4 metals.
Check that yours looks like this:

Metals
• zinc
• iron
• magnesium
• copper

Solutions
• copper sulphate
• magnesium sulphate
• iron sulphate
• zinc sulphate

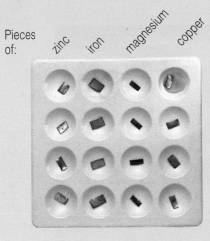

Pieces of: zinc iron magnesium copper

add copper sulphate solution

add magnesium sulphate solution

add iron sulphate solution

add zinc sulphate solution

Now you have added each solution to each metal.
Have there been any reactions?

Yes ✓   No ✗

Fill in the table with ticks or crosses:

	zinc	iron	magnesium	copper	
				✗	copper sulphate
			✗		magnesium sulphate
		✗			iron sulphate
	✗				zinc sulphate

e   Write a word equation for each reaction.

f   Which of these rules is the correct one?
  i) Less reactive metals displace reactive ones.
  ii) Reactive metals displace less reactive ones.
  Copy out the correct rule.

Things to do

1   Copy and complete:
In a reaction, a metal high in the Reactivity Series . . . . one below it. For example, ... could displace iron in a reaction.

2   Predict whether reactions will take place between these substances:
a)   copper + zinc sulphate
b)   iron + copper oxide
c)   magnesium + iron nitrate
d)   iron + potassium chloride
e)   tin + magnesium oxide
f)   zinc + copper oxide.

3   The metal nickel does not react with iron oxide. Nickel reacts with copper oxide.
a)   Copy and complete:
  nickel + copper oxide → . . . . + ...
b)   Explain why nickel won't react with iron oxide.
c)   Alongside which metal would you put nickel in the Reactivity Series?

4   Carbon is an important non-metal. How could you put it in its right position in the Reactivity Series? What experiments could you do?

Questions

1 What do you think each of the following words means?
Write no more than 2 lines for each.
a) atom b) molecule c) element d) compound e) mixture.

2 The 8 sentences below are about the process for getting pure salt from rock salt. Put the sentences in the right order so that the information makes sense.
Copy out the sentences when you have the right order.
- Rock salt is crushed into small pieces.
- The mixture is filtered.
- The solution is evaporated gently to leave dry salt.
- The pure salt dissolves.
- The mixture is warmed and stirred.
- The salt solution passes through the filter paper.
- Water is added to the mixture.
- The sand and dirt collect in the filter paper.

3 A sample of crude oil was found to contain the following:

Substance	Amount in crude oil (%)
refinery gas	0.2
gasoline	30.0
naphtha	7.0
kerosine	10.0
diesel oil	30.0
fuel oil	20.0
lubricating oil	2.0
bitumen	0.8

Put this information in the form of a bar-chart.

4 Metals can be mixed together to make **alloys**.
Find out the metals in each one of these alloys:
a) brass
b) solder
c) bronze
d) duralumin.
Write down one use for each of the alloys.

5 Plan an investigation to put the following materials into an order of hardness:

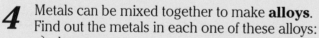

copper   iron   zinc   steel

6 In the Reactivity Series, carbon is usually placed just above iron.
Carbon and copper oxide are both black powders. Unfortunately the labels have come off their containers in the laboratory.
What experiments could you do to find out which powder is which?

Glossary

Abrasion
When a surface is worn away by rubbing.

Absorb
When light, sound or another form of energy is taken in by something, e.g. black paper absorbs light energy, or when digested food is absorbed into the blood from the small intestine.

Acid
A sour substance which can attack metal, clothing or skin. The chemical opposite of an alkali.
When an acid is dissolved in water its solution has a pH number less than 7.

Adaptation
A feature that helps a plant or an animal to survive in changing conditions.

Adolescence
The time of change from a child to an adult, when both our bodies and our emotions change.

Air resistance
A force, due to friction with the air, which pushes against a moving object, e.g. air resistance slows down a parachute.

Alkali
The chemical opposite of an acid. A base which dissolves in water. Its solution has a pH number more than 7.

Amphibian
An animal that lives on land and in water. It has moist skin and breeds in water.

Artery
A blood vessel that carries blood away from the heart.

Asteroids
Small planets and pieces of rock hurtling through space. There is a belt of asteroids between Mars and Jupiter in the Solar System.

Atmosphere
A mixture of gases, consisting of about four-fifths nitrogen and one-fifth oxygen, that surrounds the Earth.

Atom
The smallest part of an element. All atoms contain protons and electrons.

Axis
The Earth spins on its axis. It is an imaginary line passing through the Earth from the North Pole to the South Pole.

Bacteria
Microbes made up of one cell, visible with a microscope. Bacteria can grow quickly and some of them cause disease, e.g. pneumonia.

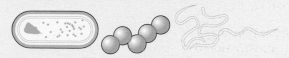

Balanced forces
Forces are balanced when they cancel out each other. The object stays still, or continues to move at a steady speed in a straight line.

Boiling point
The temperature at which a liquid boils and changes into a gas.

Braking distance
The distance a car travels *after* the brake is pressed.

Bronchus
One of the tubes at the bottom of the wind-pipe (trachea) that lead to the lungs.

wind-pipe (trachea)

ribs

bronchi

lung

Capillaries
Tiny blood vessels that let substances like oxygen, food and carbon dioxide pass into and out of the blood.

Carbohydrate
Your body's fuel. Food like glucose that gives you your energy.

Carnivores
Animals that eat only other animals – meat-eaters.

Caustic
A caustic substance is corrosive.

Cell membrane
The structure that surrounds a cell and controls what goes in and out.

Cell wall
The strong layer on the outside of a plant cell that supports the cell.

Cells
The 'building blocks' of life, made up of a cell membrane, cytoplasm and nucleus.

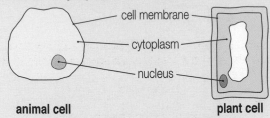

animal cell plant cell

Chemical change
A change which makes a new substance, e.g. coal burning.

Chemical energy
The energy stored in substances, e.g. foods and fuels are useful stores of chemical energy.

Chlorophyll
A green chemical in plants used to trap light energy for photosynthesis.

Chloroplasts
Tiny, round structures found inside plant cells. They capture light energy and use it to make food in photosynthesis.

Classify
To sort things out into different groups or sets.

Combustion
The reaction which occurs when a substance burns in oxygen, giving out heat energy.

Component
One of the parts that make up an electric circuit, e.g. battery, switch, bulb.

Compound
A substance made when 2 or more elements are chemically joined together, e.g. water is a compound made from hydrogen and oxygen.

Conductor
An electrical conductor allows a current to flow through it. A thermal conductor allows heat energy to pass through it. All metals are good conductors.

Constellation
A group of stars that are not necessarily close to each other, but have been thought to represent an animal, an everyday object or a mythical person and have been given a name (mostly by the ancient Greeks).

Corrosive
A corrosive substance can eat away another substance by attacking it chemically.

Cytoplasm
The jelly-like part of the cell where many chemical reactions take place.

Diffusion
The process of particles moving and mixing of their own accord, without being stirred or shaken.

Digestion
Breaking down food so that it is small enough to pass through the gut into the blood.

Dispersion
The splitting of a beam of white light into the 7 colours of the spectrum, by passing it through a prism.

Displacement
When one element takes the place of another in a compound. For example,

$$\text{magnesium} + \text{copper sulphate} \rightarrow \text{magnesium sulphate} + \text{copper}$$

This is called a displacement reaction.

Dissipation of energy
When energy is spread out by being transferred to lots of different places.

Distillation
A way to separate a liquid from a mixture of liquids, by boiling off the substances at different temperatures.

Dormant
Inactive, e.g. a dormant volcano is one which has not erupted for a long time.

Drag
Friction caused by an object travelling through a liquid or gas. For example, friction caused by air resistance.

Dynamo
A machine that transfers kinetic energy to electrical energy.

Eclipse
A *lunar eclipse* is when the shadow of the Earth falls on the Moon.

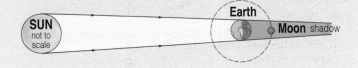

A *solar eclipse* is when the Sun is blotted out (totally or partially) by the Moon.

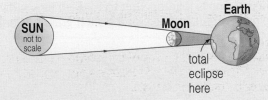

Egestion
Getting rid of indigestible food from the gut.

Egg
Female sex cell.

Electric current
A flow of electric charges (electrons). It is measured in amps (A) by an ammeter.

Electro-magnet
A coil of wire becomes a magnet when a current flows through it.

Electron
A tiny particle with a negative charge.

Element
A substance that is made of only one type of atom.

Embryo
A fertilised egg grows into an embryo and eventually into a baby.

Energy transfer
See *Transfer of energy.*

Enzymes
Chemicals that act like catalysts to speed up digestion of our food.

Equation
A shorthand way of showing the changes that take place in a chemical reaction

e.g.   iron + sulphur →   iron sulphide
         Fe   +   S   →   FeS

Equilibrium
A balanced situation, when all the forces cancel out each other.

Erosion
The wearing away of rocks.

Excretion
The loss of waste substances made in the cells during chemical reactions.

Exhale
To breathe out.

Exothermic
A reaction that *gives out* heat energy to the surroundings.

Fat
Food used as a store of energy and to insulate our bodies so we lose less heat.

Fermentation
The reaction when sugar is turned into alcohol.

Fertilisation
When sex cells join together to make a new individual, e.g. a sperm and an egg, or a pollen grain nucleus and an ovule nucleus.

Fertilisers
The nutrients that can be added to the soil if they are in short supply.

Fetus
An embryo that has developed its main features, e.g. in humans after about 3 months.

Fibre
Food that we get from plants that cannot be digested. It gives the gut muscles something to push against.

Filtration
A process used to separate undissolved solids from liquids.

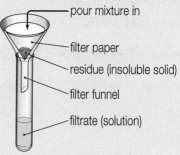

pour mixture in
filter paper
residue (insoluble solid)
filter funnel
filtrate (solution)

Flowers
The organs that many plants use to reproduce by making seeds.

Food chain
A diagram that shows how food energy is passed between plants and animals.

Food web
A diagram that shows a number of food chains linked together.

Fossil
The remains of an animal or plant which have been preserved in rocks.

Fossil fuels
A fuel made from the remains of plants and animals that died millions of years ago, e.g. coal, oil, natural gas.

Frequency
The number of complete vibrations in each second. A sound with a high frequency has a high pitch.

Friction
A force when 2 surfaces rub together. It always pushes against the movement.

Fuel
A substance that is burned in air (oxygen) to give out energy.

Fungi
Moulds, such as yeast or mushrooms, that produce spores.

Fungicide
A chemical which kills fungi that attack crops.

Fuse
A safety device in an electrical circuit. It is a piece of wire that heats up and melts, breaking the circuit, if too much current passes through it.

Gamete
The male or female reproductive cells.

Gas
A substance which is light, has the shape of its container and is easily squashed. The particles in a gas are far apart. They move quickly and in all directions.

Gestation
The time from fertilisation to birth, e.g. in humans the gestation period is about 40 weeks.

Gravity, gravitational force
A force of attraction between 2 objects. The pull of gravity on you is your weight.

Habitat
The place where a plant or animal lives.

Haemoglobin
The substance in red blood cells that transports oxygen around the body.

Herbicide
A chemical used to kill weeds that are in competition with a crop.

Herbivores
Animals that eat only plants.

Hibernate
To remain inactive throughout the winter months.

Igneous rock
A rock formed by molten (melted) material cooling down.

Image
When you look in a mirror, you see an image of yourself.

Inhale
To breathe in.

Indicator
A substance that changes colour depending on the pH of the solution you add it to.

Insecticide
A chemical that kills insects that feed on crops.

Inspire
To breathe in.

Insulator
An electrical insulator does not allow a current to flow easily. A thermal insulator does not let heat energy flow easily.

Intestine
Tube below the stomach where food is digested and absorbed.

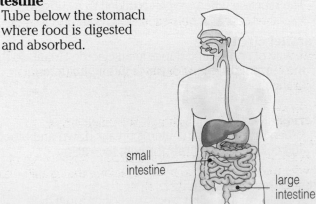

small intestine

large intestine

Invertebrate
An animal without a backbone.

Kilowatt hour
The unit used to measure electrical energy. It is the amount of energy transferred when 1000 joules of energy pass each second for one hour. One kilowatt hour is equal to $1000 \times 60 \times 60 = 3\,600\,000$ joules

Kinetic energy
The energy of something which is moving.

Law of reflection
When light rays bounce off a mirror:

angle of incidence = angle of reflection.

Lava
Molten rock ejected from a volcano.

Lever
A simple machine that produces a bigger force or movement than we apply.

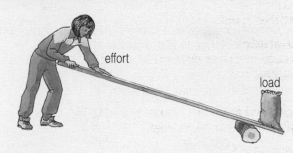

effort

load

Liquid
A substance which has the shape of its container, can be poured and is not easily squashed. The particles in a liquid are quite close together but free to move.

Lungs
The organs in our body that collect oxygen and get rid of carbon dioxide.

Magma
Hot molten rock below the Earth's surface.

Magnetic field
The area round a magnet where it attracts or repels another magnet.

Magnetic material
A substance which is attracted by a magnet, e.g. iron and steel.

Magnify
To make bigger.

Mammal
Warm-blooded animals with fur or hair that suckle their young.

Mammary glands
Where mammals produce the milk for their young.

Melting point
The temperature at which a solid melts and changes into a liquid.

Menstruation
The discharge of blood and lining of the uterus from the vagina.
This happens at the end of each menstrual cycle in which an egg has not been fertilised.

Metal
An element which is a good conductor and is usually shiny, e.g. copper.

Metamorphic rock
A rock formed by heating and compressing (squeezing) an existing rock.

Migration
Moving from one place to another in different seasons to avoid adverse or harsh conditions.

Millennium (plural: millennia)
A period of one thousand years.

Mixture
A substance made when some elements or compounds are mixed together. It is *not* a pure substance.

Molecule
A group of atoms joined together.

oxygen atom

a molecule of water, H₂O

hydrogen atom

Muscle
Structures that contract and relax to move bones at joints.

National Grid
A network of cables, mostly running above ground on pylons, that connects all of the power stations throughout the country with consumers.

Neutral
Something which is neither an acid nor an alkali.

Neutralisation
The chemical reaction of an acid with a base, in which they cancel each other out.

Non-metal
An element which does not conduct electricity.
(The exception to this is graphite – a form of carbon which is a non-metal, but it does conduct.)

Non-renewable resources
Energy sources that are used up and not replaced, e.g. fossil fuels.

Nucleus of a cell
A round structure that controls the cell and contains the instructions to make more cells.

Nutrients
The chemicals needed by plants for healthy growth, e.g. nitrates, phosphates.

Omnivores
Animals that eat both plants and animals.

Opaque
An opaque object will not let light pass through it.

Orbit
The path of a planet or a satellite.
Its shape is usually an ellipse (oval).

ellipse

Organ
A structure made up of different tissues that work together to do a particular job.

Organism
A living thing, such as a plant, an animal or a microbe.

Ovary
Where the eggs are made in a female.

Oviduct
A tube that carries an egg from the ovary to the uterus.

Oxidation
The reaction when oxygen is added to a substance.

Parallel circuit
A way of connecting things in an electric circuit, so that the current divides and passes through different branches.

Period
When the lining of the uterus breaks down and blood and cells leave the body through the vagina.

Pesticide
A chemical that kills insects, weeds or fungi that damage crops.

pH number
A number which shows how strong an acid or alkali is.
Acids have pH less than 7.
Alkalis have pH greater than 7.

Photosynthesis
The process by which green plants use light energy to turn carbon dioxide and water into sugars:

carbon dioxide + water $\xrightarrow[\text{chlorophyll}]{\text{light and}}$ sugar + oxygen

Physical change
A change in which no new substance is made.
The substance just changes to a different state, e.g. water boiling.

Pitch
A whistle has a high pitch, a bass guitar has a low pitch.

Placenta
A structure that forms in the uterus allowing the blood of the baby and the blood of the mother to come close together.

Pollination
The transfer of pollen from the anthers to the stigma of a flower.

Porosity
The ability to absorb a liquid such as water, e.g. sandstone is a porous rock.

Potential energy
Stored energy, e.g. a bike at the top of a hill has gravitational potential energy.

Prediction
A statement that describes and explains what you think will happen in an investigation.

Principle of conservation of energy
The amount of energy before a transfer is always equal to the amount of energy after the transfer. The energy is 'conserved'.

Producers
Green plants that make their own food by photosynthesis.

Product
A substance made as a result of a chemical reaction.

Protein
Food needed for the growth and repair of cells.

Puberty
The age at which the sexual organs become developed.

Pumice
A light, porous rock formed from lava.

Radiation
Rays of light, X-rays, radio waves, etc., including the transfer of energy through a vacuum.

Reaction
A chemical change which makes a new substance.

Reactivity series
A list of elements in order of their reactivity. The most reactive element is put at the top of the list.

Reduction
A reaction when oxygen is removed, e.g. copper oxide is *reduced* to copper.

Reflection
When light bounces off an object.

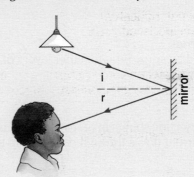

Refraction
A ray of light passing from one substance into another is bent (refracted).

Renewable energy resources
Energy sources that do not get used up, e.g. solar energy, wind, waves, tides, etc.

Reptile
An animal with dry, scaly skin that lays eggs with soft shells.

Resistance
A thin wire gives more resistance to an electric current than a thick wire.

Respiration

The release of energy from food in our cells. Usually using up oxygen and producing carbon dioxide.

glucose + oxygen ⟶ carbon dioxide + water + energy

Resultant force

The result of *unbalanced forces*.

Rock cycle

A cycle that means that one type of rock can be changed into another type of rock over a period of time.

Salt

A substance made when an acid and a base react together.

Satellite

An object that goes round a planet or a star, e.g. the Moon goes round the Earth.

Saturated solution

A solution in which no more solute can dissolve at that temperature.

Scattering

When rays of light hit a rough surface (like paper) they reflect off in all directions.

Sedimentary rock

A rock formed by squashing together layers of material that settle out in water.

Series circuit

A way of connecting things in an electric circuit, so that the current flows through each one in turn.

Skeleton

A rigid internal or external framework that protects organs and provides a means of attachment for muscles, forming a system of joints and levers to allow movement.

Solar System

The Sun and all 9 planets that go round it.

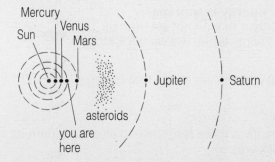

Solid

A substance which has a fixed shape, is not runny and is not squashed easily. The particles in a solid are packed very closely together – they vibrate but do not move from place to place.

Soluble

Describes something which dissolves, e.g. salt is soluble in water.

Solute

The solid that dissolves to make a solution.

Solution

The clear liquid made when a solute dissolves in a solvent, e.g. salt (solute) dissolves in water (solvent) to make salt solution.

Solvent

The liquid that dissolves the solute to make a solution.

Species

A type of living thing that breeds and produces fertile offspring.

Spectrum

The colours of the rainbow that can be separated when white light is passed through a prism: red, orange, yellow, green, blue, indigo, violet (ROY G. BIV).

Speed

How fast an object is moving.

$$\text{Speed} = \frac{\text{distance travelled}}{\text{time taken}}$$

Sperm

Male sex cell.

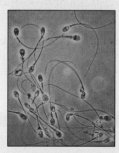

States of matter
The 3 states in which matter can be found: *solid*, *liquid* and *gas*.

Temperature
How hot or cold something is.
It is measured in °C, using a thermometer.

Testis
Where the sperms are made in a male.

Thermal energy
Another name for heat energy.

Thermal transfer
When a cup of tea cools down, there is a transfer of thermal energy (heat) from the cup to the surroundings. This transfer can be by conduction, convection, radiation and evaporation.

Thinking distance
The distance travelled in a car during the driver's reaction time.

Tissue
A group of similar cells that look the same and do the same job.

Trachea
The wind-pipe taking air to and from the lungs.

Transfer of energy
The movement of energy from one place to another, for a job to be done.

Transformation of energy
When energy changes from one form to another, e.g. when paper burns, chemical energy is changed to heat and light energy.

Transformer
A device that either increases (step-up transformer) or decreases (step-down transformer) the voltage of electricity.

Translucent
A material that is translucent allows light to pass through, but an object cannot be seen clearly.

Transparent
A material that is transparent allows light to pass through so an object can be seen clearly.

Unbalanced forces
If 2 forces do not cancel out each other, they are unbalanced. There will be a resultant force. The object will change its speed or change its direction.

Universal indicator
A liquid which changes colour when acids or alkalis are added to it. It shows whether the acid or alkali is strong or weak.

Uterus
The womb, where a fertilised egg settles and grows into a baby.

Vacuole
The space in a plant cell that is filled with a watery solution called cell sap.

Vein
A blood vessel that carries blood back to the heart.

Vertebrate
An animal that has a backbone.

Vibrating
Moving backwards and forwards quickly, e.g. the particles in a solid vibrate.

Viruses
Extremely small microbes which are not visible with a microscope. Many viruses spread disease by invading cells and copying themselves, e.g. influenza.

Vitamins
Complex chemicals needed in small amounts to keep us healthy, e.g. vitamin C.

Weathering
The crumbling away of rocks caused by weather conditions such as wind and rain.

Index